QUEST

LITERACY ACTIVITY BOOK

Senior Authors
J. David Cooper
John J. Pikulski

Authors
Kathryn H. Au
Margarita Calderón
Jacqueline C. Comas
Marjorie Y. Lipson
J. Sabrina Mims
Susan E. Page
Sheila W. Valencia
MaryEllen Vogt

Consultants
Dolores Malcolm
Tina Saldivar
Shane Templeton

INVITATIONS
TO LITERACY

Houghton Mifflin Company • Boston

Atlanta • Dallas • Geneva, Illinois • Palo Alto • Princeton

1997 Impression
Copyright © 1996 by Houghton Mifflin Company. All rights reserved.

Printed in the U.S.A.

ISBN: 0-395-72487-2

11 12 13 14 15 -WC- 02 01 00 99 98

CONTENTS

CONTENTS

My Reading Strategy Guide

Strategy	What I Do As I Read	✔
Predict/Infer	Note important information. Relate illustrations to the selection. Consider what I already know. Think about what may happen.	☐ ☐ ☐ ☐
Self-Question	Ask myself what I want to learn.	☐
Think About Words	Use context and word parts to give meaning to unfamiliar words.	☐
Monitor	Read ahead. Look at the illustrations. Reread text that is unclear or confusing. Ask myself if it makes sense. Ask myself if I am learning what I want to know. Ask for help if I need it.	☐ ☐ ☐ ☐ ☐ ☐
Summarize	Summarize as I read. Summarize after I read. Note main idea. Note important details.	☐ ☐ ☐ ☐
Evaluate	Ask myself how I feel about what I read. Ask myself whether I agree or disagree with all or part of what I read. Ask myself whether I learned what I wanted to know.	☐ ☐ ☐ ☐

Name

School in Summertime

Write each word in the correct sentence. Then write a definition for the word.

| hovered | oblivious | profusely | replica |

1 Huge paper birds _____ over our heads as we worked on our

clay models.

Definition: _____

_____

2 I used red clay to make a _____ of our school building.

Definition: _____

_____

3 I was sweating _____ by the time I got home for lunch because I

had to walk in the July sun.

Definition: _____

_____

4 Some of the students were so absorbed in making their clay models that they were

_____ of the four o'clock bell; they did not realize that class was

over for the day.

Definition: _____

_____

Name _____

Making the Grade

Fill in this log by telling what happens to the narrator in each class. What happens at the talent show?

SUMMER SCHOOL LOG	
Science	
History	
German	
Square Dancing	
Talent Show	

....
Name

The Writing Process

Prewriting
Choose my topic.
Plan my writing.

Drafting
Get my ideas down on paper.
Don't worry about mistakes.

Revising
Read my draft thoughtfully.
Clarify my ideas.
Check my organization.
Replace weak words.

Proofreading
Read my draft carefully.
Use proofreading marks.
Check for correct sentences.
Check and correct spelling, punctuation, and capitalization.

Publishing and Sharing
Think of a good title.
Make a clean copy.
Check it over.
Share my writing.

Name _____

What Do You Think?

Choose a Topic List three or four possible topics for writing about a vacation activity.

_____   _____

_____   _____

Circle the one you decide to write about.

Plan Your Writing Make a web to plan and organize your ideas. Write your topic in the middle. Put main ideas in circles around it. Add circles for details that connect to each main idea.

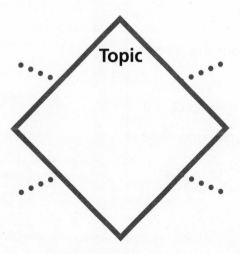

Now think about a good order for your main ideas. Number the parts of your web in that order.

Name

Revising Your Writing

Reread and revise your writing, using the Revising Checklist as a guide. Then have a writing conference with a partner. Help each other by using the Questions for a Writing Conference.

• Revising Checklist •

❏ Have I stated my main ideas clearly?

❏ Have I given enough details and support?

❏ Have I made clear why I enjoy this activity?

❏ Should I leave out anything?

❏ Are my main ideas and details in good order?

❏ Have I used strong and interesting words?

Questions for a Writing Conference

• What is the best thing about this piece of writing?

• Does the writing keep to the topic?

• Is the piece well organized?

• Is it clear what the writer is trying to express?

• What information could be deleted? Where is more needed?

• Are the words well chosen? Which ones could be stronger and more interesting?

My Notes Write down ideas from your writing conference.

_____

_____

_____

_____

_____

_____

_____

_____

_____

_____

_____

Name

Survival!

What elements do most survival tales have in common? After reading each selection, take a few minutes to note specific examples of these elements from each tale.

	Bearstone	Tonweya and the Eagles
The main character faces a life-and-death problem.		
The main character uses intelligence to solve the problem.		
Luck also plays a role in the survival of the characters.		
The main character survives with help from others.		

Name _____

Survival!

What elements do most survival tales have in common? After reading each selection, take a few minutes to note specific examples of these elements from each tale.

	Island of the Blue Dolphins	Maniac Magee
The main character faces a life-and-death problem.		
The main character uses intelligence to solve the problem.		
Luck also plays a role in the survival of the characters.		
The main character survives with help from others.		

Name

A Mountain Adventure

You have just hiked in the mountains of Colorado for the first time.
Address the envelope to a friend. Then complete the letter using the
vocabulary words.

| trailhead | claustrophobic | wilderness | canyon | rapids | veered |

_____

_____

_____

_____

_____

Dear _____,

    I finally got to the mountains! Gran and I packed our backpacks
and looked for the welcome sign that showed the _____.
After a while, we came to the edge of a steep rocky
_____. Looking down, we saw a river with white water
rushing over rocks. Gran said we'd have to go past these
_____ before we crossed the river.

    When we moved on, the trail _____ sharply to the
left at a huge rock. We went right through it! Inside the small, dark
tunnel of rock I felt so _____ that I couldn't wait to get
out. Outside, we saw a wonderful sight—a blue lake, green meadows,
and high peaks. I guess I've discovered that I prefer the natural
_____ to the big city.

Name

Did It Really Happen?

The sentences tell about Cloyd and Walter. Write **T** if the sentence is true, or **F** if the sentence is false. If a sentence is false, correct it to make it true.

1 _____ Cloyd and Walter are going to explore an old farm of Walter's family.

_____

2 _____ Before their journey begins, Cloyd and Walter visit a cemetery where Walter's wife is buried.

_____

3 _____ Cloyd shows Walter an eagle feather he found in a cave.

_____

4 _____ Cloyd and Walter use a truck to carry their equipment and food.

_____

5 _____ While they are traveling, Cloyd enjoys hunting for deer.

_____

6 _____ Cloyd gets caught in a sudden hailstorm and falls and hurts his leg.

_____

7 _____ Cloyd nearly dies because his body gets too cold.

_____

8 _____ Cloyd's life is saved by Walter, who finds him in the meadow.

_____

9 _____ Walter never finds Cloyd after the big storm.

_____

10 _____ At the end, Cloyd thanks the man who saved his life.

_____

Name

Help! Help!

As you know, readers add selection details to personal knowledge to predict outcomes. Read the paragraphs about a life-threatening situation. Then answer the questions about your prediction and how you arrived at it.

Evan had never seen so much water. Water in the kitchen, up the stairs, and finally, water in the bedrooms, as the Crooked River rose and rose like a hungry beast. Evan and his father climbed onto the slippery shingles of the roof and held on to the wet bricks of the chimney. "Help!" Evan screamed.

"Don't waste your energy!" his father shouted. "There's no one around!" Evan clung to his father's shirt while the rain stung his face. In the distance, Evan heard a new sound. It was not the slosh of water against the furniture. It was not the rain slapping the windows or the roof. It was a motorboat and a dog barking. It was a bullhorn and a human voice!

WHAT?

WHAT DO YOU THINK WILL HAPPEN?

WHY?

WHAT DETAILS DID YOU USE TO PREDICT THIS OUTCOME?

HOW?

WHAT DO YOU ALREADY KNOW THAT HELPED YOU MAKE YOUR PREDICTION?

Heads or Tails?

Prepare the trout for the frying pan by adding the necessary
ingredients. Use proofreading marks when you add subjects
or predicates, capital letters, and end punctuation.

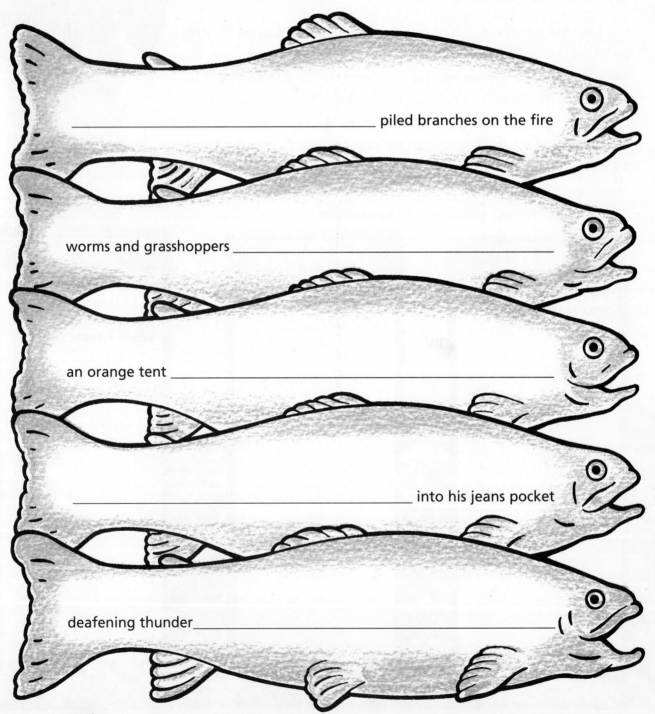

_____ piled branches on the fire

worms and grasshoppers _____

an orange tent _____

_____ into his jeans pocket

deafening thunder_____

Splish Splash

Cloyd's diary got soaked in the storm. Help him fix it by
circling the twenty words with *-ed, -ing, -es, -s, -er,* or *-est*
endings. Rewrite them in the correct column in the chart.

Wednesday 6:00

Walter and I are making a trip up to the mine.
He stopped at the cemetery first to visit his wife.
The sky suddenly got darker, and I looked up and
saw big, black clouds moving toward us. Thunder
rumbled, so we started running for the truck. Rain
poured down, and the biggest drops I've ever seen
fell in sheets on the windshield.

We're at our campsite now, and the rain has
finally passed. Walter always goes to bed earlier
than I do, and he's already snoring away. I
should go to sleep myself. Tomorrow will be a long
day. I hear wolves howling in the distance. I
hope they're not hungry for campers tonight!

-ed	-ing	-s/-es	-er	-est

Name

Walter Is to Cloyd . . .

Circle the pair of words that completes each analogy.

1. **peak** is to **canyon** as
   a. **valley** is to **river**
   b. **forest** is to **clearing**
   c. **attic** is to **cellar**

2. **swerved** is to **veered** as
   a. **dozed** is to **slept**
   b. **trout** is to **fish**
   c. **survived** is to **died**

3. **claustrophobic** is to **tunnel** as
   a. **seasick** is to **ocean**
   b. **worried** is to **ocean**
   c. **mountain** is to **backpack**

4. **rapids** is to **calm** as
   a. **jungle** is to **clear**
   b. **tent** is to **shelter**
   c. **river** is to **stream**

5. **trailhead** is to **hiker** as
   a. **finish line** is to **racer**
   b. **packhorse** is to **rider**
   c. **page one** is to **reader**

6. **unsettled** is to **wilderness** as
   a. **populated** is to **city**
   b. **barren** is to **desert**
   c. **gravestone** is to **cemetery**

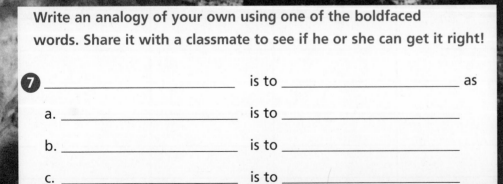

Write an analogy of your own using one of the boldfaced
words. Share it with a classmate to see if he or she can get it right!

7. _____ is to _____ as

   a. _____ is to _____

   b. _____ is to _____

   c. _____ is to _____

Name _____

Wilderness Words

Words with *ie* or *ei* Each Spelling Word has the *ie* or *ei* vowel combination. Each word follows this familiar rule: Use *i* before *e* except after *c* or in words with the |ā| sound, as in *weigh*. You must memorize any exceptions to this rule.

Complete each Spelling Word by writing *ie* or *ei* on each map. Then write each Spelling Word on the correct backpack.

Spelling Words

1. piece
2. eight
3. believe
4. weight
5. reins
6. brief
7. relieve
8. sleigh
9. receive
10. ceiling

My Study List
What other words do you need to study for spelling? Add them to My Study List for Bearstone in the back of this book.

sl____gh

c____ling

rel____ve

bel____ve

br____f

p____ce

rec____ve

r____ns

w____ght

____ght

i before e

1 _____
2 _____
3 _____
4 _____

ei after c

5 _____
6 _____

|ā| ei

7 _____
8 _____
9 _____
10 _____

Name

Spelling Spree

Spelling Words

1. piece
2. eight
3. believe
4. weight
5. reins
6. brief
7. relieve
8. sleigh
9. receive
10. ceiling

Proofreading   Circle the five misspelled
Spelling Words on this trail sign. Then write
each word correctly.

Weminuche Wilderness Area
This year, this area will receive thousands of
visitors. We beleave you can help us keep it
beautiful. Please do not tie packhorses to the
trees, as the reigns scar the bark. Before leaving,
give your campsite a breif check. Don't leave
even one peece of litter! If you are traveling by
sliegh, keep horses and sleds on the trail.
Remember, this is YOUR wilderness!

1 _____

2 _____

3 _____

4 _____

5 _____

Spelling Trails Follow the directions to write Spelling Words.

6 Write the word that means "to ease."   _____

7 Change the middle three letters of answer
number 6 to write a word that means "to
get or acquire something."   _____

8 Find the middle three letters of answer number 7.
Add four letters to write the word that means
"the inside upper surface of a room."   _____

9 Write the word that means "the heaviness
of an object."   _____

10 Drop one letter from answer number 9 to
write a word that means "a number equal
to the sum of 7 + 1."   _____

 Last Words An epitaph is a gravestone inscription written in
memory of the dead person. On a separate piece of paper, write the
epitaph that might go on Walter's grave. Use Spelling Words from the list.

The Great Sentence Divide

Subjects and Predicates The dotted line on the map shows the location of the Continental Divide in the United States. Write the complete subjects on the western side of the Divide and the complete predicates on the eastern side. Then connect the dots to trace the Divide.

Example: The Divide is a series of mountain ridges.

1. It extends from Mexico to Alaska.

2. Some rivers have their source here.

3. Their waters flow east or west of the Divide.

4. Trails are popular with hikers.

5. Several people have hiked from Mexico to Canada.

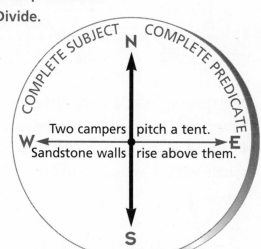

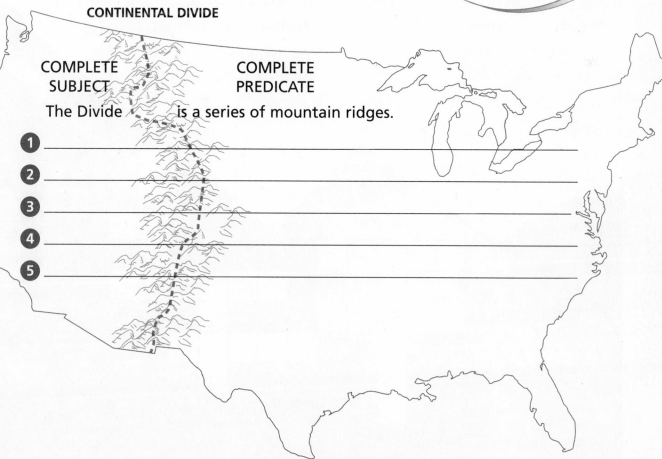

Name

Puzzling Subjects

The **guide was watching** for mud slides.

Simple Subject	**Simple Predicate**
guide	was watching

Subjects and Predicates Draw one line under the simple subject and two lines under the simple predicate in each sentence. Then fill in the puzzle with the simple subjects. Match the numbers in the puzzle with the numbers of the sentences.

Across

2. It had been a clear and sunny morning.

3. The horses' packs were tied securely.

5. The horses with their packs could lose their footing in the mud.

7. A storm might start.

8. The narrow trail wound through the forest.

Down

1. Our guide was leading two packhorses.

4. Some dark clouds gathered on the horizon.

6. A strong, heavy rain had been spotted in the mountains above.

Eagles in the Nests

Read the words in each nest from "Tonweya and the Eagles." Then write three words from the list that are related in meaning. Use a dictionary if necessary.

crack	perpendicular	divine	with empty stomach
rebelliously	daringly	straight up	boldly
hungrily	hallowed	opening	honored
narrow hole	greedily	steep	

sacred

_____

_____

_____

sheer

_____

_____

_____

defiantly

_____

_____

cleft

_____

_____

_____

ravenously

_____

_____

_____

Name

Friends with the Eagles

**Answer the questions about the characters, plot, and setting of
"Tonweya and the Eagles."**

Chano's Story

What is Chano's family doing at the beginning of this selection?_____

_____

What does Chano see that prompts his father to tell a story?_____

_____

Tonweya's Story

How does Tonweya get trapped on the rocky ledge?_____

_____

What does Tonweya feed the two eaglets?_____

How does Tonweya stay warm on the cold night?_____

How does Tonweya escape the ledge and survive?_____

_____

What are the first two things Tonweya does after he escapes the ledge?_____

_____

How does Tonweya decorate the eagles to honor them?_____

_____

What does Tonweya eventually do with the eagles?_____

_____

Chano's Story

What does Chano's father believe about the eagles? _____

_____

Name

The Inside Story

Read aloud the story within a story. Then complete the graphic organizer with the details from both stories. Compare your chart with a classmate's.

The Good Idea

"Someone should make all these leaves disappear," said Jenny one chilly October day. She and her uncle were raking his big yard.

"Well, that's a good idea," said her uncle, "but ideas aren't worth much unless you figure out how to make them happen. Let me tell you a story about good ideas."

Once upon a time, a group of mice lived in constant fear of a huge, ravenous cat. One day they had a meeting in their mouse hole to come up with ideas for a better life. One young mouse suggested that they hang a bell around the cat's neck so they could hear her coming.

"Great idea!" the mice cheered. Their worries were over.

"But wait," an old wise mouse said. "Who will put the bell on the cat?" All of the mice were silent. Each one looked at the others. No one wanted to bell the cat.

"Oh, I get it," Jenny smiled . . . and kept raking.

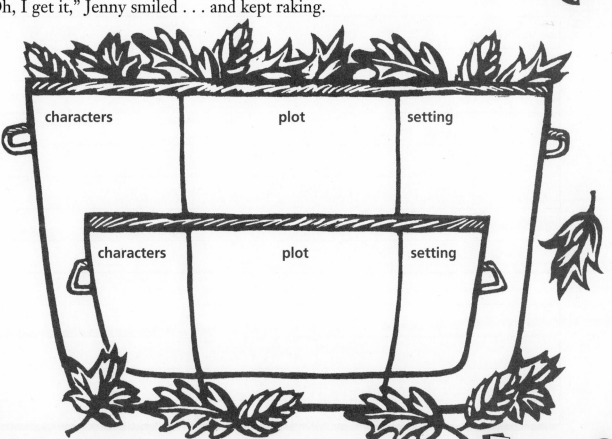

Name

Put It Together!

Revise this story about Tonweya. Combine sentences to create
compound subjects and compound predicates.

Tonweya cried for help. Tonweya got no reply.
He thought about climbing up the cliff wall. The
wall was very steep. It didn't have any handholds
or footholds. He was trapped. The ledge was very
narrow. It was too small to sleep on safely. The night was raw and
chilly. The eagles nestled closer. Tonweya nestled closer. They kept
each other warm. Tonweya could fight for survival. He could give
up. He could die. He started feeding rawhide to the baby eagles.
The eagles were getting bigger. The eagles were growing stronger.
Every day Tonweya held the eagles up. He let them try their wings.
The eagles finally flew off. They carried Tonweya with them.

22   **Survival!**

Name

Soaring Syllables

Count the number of syllables in each word and write the number in the
wing tip. Hint: The total number of syllables is 25.

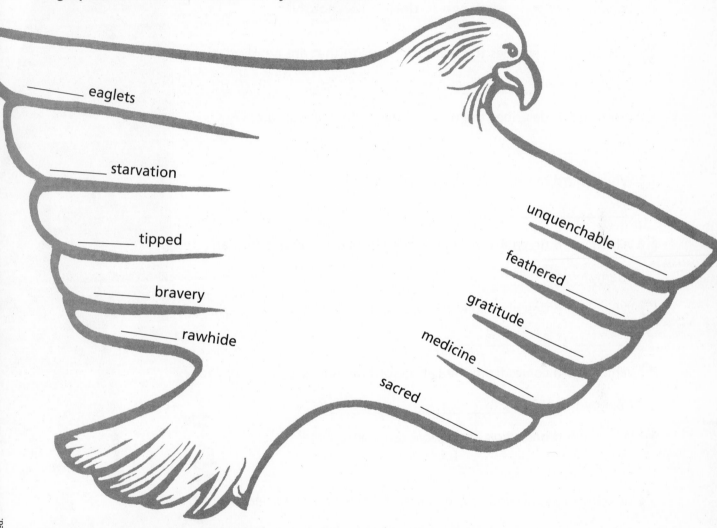

_____ eaglets

_____ starvation

_____ tipped

_____ bravery

_____ rawhide

unquenchable _____

feathered _____

gratitude _____

medicine _____

sacred _____

Read the haiku about Tonweya. Then complete the rule about haikus
by filling in the missing numbers.

**SOARING OVERHEAD,
SACRED BIRDS OF TONWEYA
BRING THE BOY GOOD LUCK.**

Haiku poems have three lines and seventeen syllables.
The first line of a haiku has _____ syllables, the second
line has _____ , and the third line has _____.

Name _____

Which Word?

Answer the following questions by writing a vocabulary word.

| sacred | sheer | defiantly | cleft | ravenously |

1 Which word describes the walls of a canyon that are nearly straight up and down? _____

2 Which word describes the way a starving animal would eat?

_____

3 Which word means *steep* or *perpendicular*?

_____

4 Which word describes the way a brave underdog might face an enemy? _____

5 Which word describes something considered holy?

_____

6 Which word comes from the Latin word *raviner,* which means "to take by force"? _____

7 Which word has *union* and *whole* as its antonyms?

_____

8 Which word is related to the words *sacrifice* and *sacrament*?

_____

Write two questions of your own that use the vocabulary words:

9 Which word _____?

_____

10 Which word _____?

_____

Name

Winged Words

Final Schwa + *r* Each Spelling Word ends with the schwa sound + *r*. The schwa sound, shown as lǝl, is a weak vowel sound often found in an unstressed syllable. In words of two or more syllables, the final lǝrl sounds can be spelled with the patterns *er, or*, and *ar*.

lǝrl   dang**er**   terr**or**   li**ar**

Complete each Spelling Word by adding *er, or,* or *ar* to each word part. Then write the Spelling Words on the lines with the matching spelling pattern for the final sound.

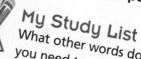

Spelling Words

1. danger
2. feather
3. shiver
4. terror
5. hunger
6. shoulder
7. quarter
8. error
9. liar
10. popular

My Study List
What other words do you need to study for spelling? Add them to My Study List for *Tonweya and the Eagles* in the back of this book.

quart_____   feath_____

terr_____   hung_____

li_____   popul_____

shiv_____   should_____

dang_____   err_____

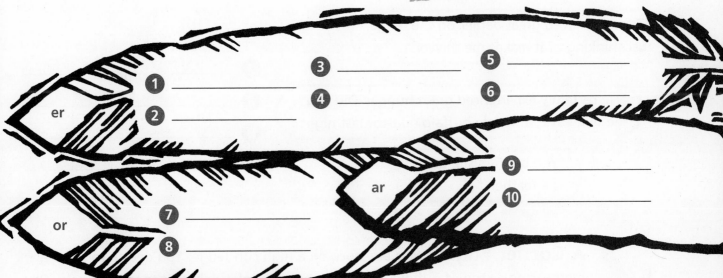

er

1 _____
2 _____

3 _____
4 _____

5 _____
6 _____

or

7 _____
8 _____

ar

9 _____
10 _____

Name

Spelling Spree

Pointed Puzzle Write the Spelling Word that fits each clue.

Spelling Words
1. danger
2. feather
3. shiver
4. terror
5. hunger
6. shoulder
7. quarter
8. error
9. liar
10. popular

1 part of a bird's outer covering

2 a mistake

3 someone who says things that are not true

4 liked by many people

5 great fear

6 body part between the neck and the upper arm

1 _____
2 _____
3 _____
4 _____
5 _____
6 _____

Proofreading Circle the four misspelled Spelling Words in this conversation. Then write each word correctly.

"Tonweya faced great danjer on the ledge. Just thinking of it makes me shivver."

"He certainly experienced great hungar. Did you see him eat that whole buffalo quartor last night?"

"Yes, but he's still as light as a feather!"

7 _____
8 _____
9 _____
10 _____

 A Carrier Eaglet You are stuck on a high cliff ledge. You decide to write a message on a strip of buffalo hide and have an eaglet deliver it to your people. On a separate sheet of paper, write your message. Use Spelling Words from the list.

All About Eagles

SENTENCES		SUBJECTS
Interrogative	What does that word mean?	word
Imperative	Find *prey* in the dictionary.	(You)

Kinds of Sentences/More Subjects Find out about the bald eagle.

On a separate piece of paper, list all the words from the boxes numbered 1.

Then do the same for the words in the boxes numbered 2, 3, 4, and 5.

5 tail	3 seen	4 this	2 It	1 the	3 you
2 bird	5 head	1 eagle	2 States	3 ever	
5 and	2 of	4 at	5 bird	1 How	2 the
1 looks	5 white	3 Have	2 United	4 Look	
2 national	5 The	1 bald	5 has	2 is	5 a
3 one	1 glorious	2 the	4 drawing		

Now rearrange each list of words to form a sentence. Add the correct end punctuation, and write *declarative, interrogative, imperative,* or *exclamatory* to tell what kind of sentence each one is. Then write the subjects of any interrogative and imperative sentences.

1 _____

_____

2 _____

_____

3 _____

_____

4 _____

_____

5 _____

_____

Name

What's in a Name?

Kinds of Sentences/More Subjects
Use each letter in the name *Tonweya* to begin a sentence about his adventure. Add correct end punctuation and write what kind of sentence each one is. Be sure to use at least one declarative, interrogative, imperative, and exclamatory sentence. Also write the subject of each interrogative and imperative sentence.

Example:

T   Tell me the story again.   imperative   (You)

1 **O** _____

_____

2 **N** _____

_____

3 **W** _____

_____

4 **E** _____

_____

5 **Y** _____

_____

6 **A** _____

_____

Name _____

Explorer's Log

You are a Spanish explorer who has discovered islands off the coast of California. Use the vocabulary words to complete your journal.

| drifted | slinking | skirted | seeping | chafing |

December 12, 1835

    We had sailed four days without seeing land. Suddenly, we spotted a group of islands. The sea was rough from last night's storm, so we _____ the shore until we found a calm place to stop.

December 13, 1835

    Today, we were very careful as we explored the island. There are very few trees to hide us from wild animals. We protected ourselves by _____ from rock to rock and carrying our weapons in hand. We heard wild dogs, but saw none.

December 16, 1835

    We discovered that two of our four ships were leaking. We emptied the boats that had water _____ in and began repairs immediately. We tied the dry boats to the rocks and hauled the others onto the beach. We worked so hard that we failed to notice that the rocks were _____ the ropes. Soon, they snapped! Imagine how foolish I felt when our good boats _____ out to sea!

Name

Living in the Wild

How do these animals and objects affect Karana? Which ones help her, and which ones hurt her? Write your answers on the lines.

FLAT ROCK

_____
_____
_____
_____

WILD DOGS

_____
_____
_____
_____

STARS

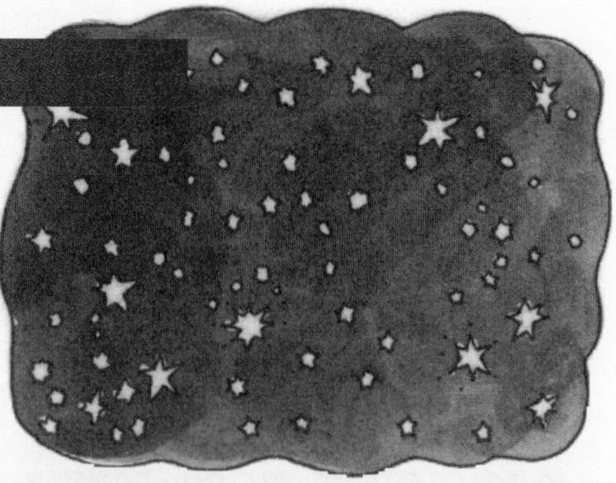

_____
_____
_____
_____

DOLPHINS

_____
_____
_____
_____

Name

Waves of Events

Just as the waves rise and fall—each one connected to the one before
and the one after—the events of a story flow together. The order of their
flow is called sequence. Choose one page from the selection and use it to
fill in the sequence chart. List the events that occur on the page. Note
time words O'Dell uses and how much time passes between events.

What happens?

Time words used?

How much time has passed since the last event?

....

Name

Jot It Down!

Read the paragraph and write an entry for a two-sided
response journal. On the left, write at least four details or
facts from the paragraph. On the right, jot down questions,
comparisons, memories, ideas, feelings, or thoughts that you
had while or after you read.

    The wind howled and the whole house shook. Would the windows break?
Would the chimney snap off? I searched the room for what I thought might be the
safest spot. Under the stairs? In a corner? Suddenly the electricity went off. As I
rummaged in the desk drawer for a candle, I heard a loud crack and then a heavy
thud. Lightning? Oh no, I said out loud, the trees are falling! The tall white pines
were breaking and thwacking the ground. They could tear apart the roof, the
walls. They could kill me.

MY RESPONSES

NOTES FROM MY READING

Message in a Bottle

**Read the message. Circle the ten words with the prefix *un-*, *pre-*,
or *re-*. Then write each word and a short definition for each
word, keeping in mind the meaning of the prefix.**

Help! I'm all alone on this island. There are unfriendly dogs here, so I had
to rearrange my camp. As a precaution, I remade my seaweed bed high up on
the rocks. It's uncomfortable, but I feel safer now. I moved my food up there too,
to prevent the dogs from getting it. I was unable to find any weapons in my
village. I'll have to return there another day to reexamine the huts. The canoes
my people hid are unsafe. I tried to cross the sea in one but had to turn back
because it leaked. Please rescue me!

1 _____

_____

2 _____

_____

3 _____

_____

4 _____

_____

5 _____

6 _____

_____

7 _____

_____

8 _____

_____

9 _____

_____

10 _____

Survival! **33**

Name

Name

Vivid Verbs

Use the proofreading mark for delete ( ) to cross out the underlined weak verbs in the sentences. Use a carat (∧) to insert a stronger vocabulary word into each sentence. Read the revised sentences aloud.

drifted
slinking
skirted
seeping
chafing

                        was seeping
Sample: Sea water ∧got through the small hole in the canoe.

1 I <u>moved</u> on a raft through ocean waters.

2 A strong wind was <u>bothering</u> my face, making it red and dry.

3 Suddenly I noticed water <u>coming</u> through the bottom of the raft!

4 The ropes were <u>rubbing</u> against each other and letting water in.

5 I was going to fix the leak when I saw a shark <u>moving</u> through the water!

6 The shark <u>went around</u> the edges of the raft.

7 I <u>went</u> farther from shore with a hungry shark nearby!

8 I hit the shark on the nose with my oar and sent it <u>swimming</u> away.

9 Then I woke up. What a dream! The rest of the night, I <u>went</u> in and out of sleep.

10 The next morning my mother asked, "Why were you yelling about a shark last night?" I <u>avoided</u> the issue.

Sealife Sort

Final Schwa + *n* or *l* Some Spelling Words
end with the schwa sound + n, shown as Iənl or Inl.
These sounds can be spelled with the pattern **on** or **en**.

Iənl or Inl   weap**on**   hidd**en**

The other Spelling Words end with the schwa sound
+ l, shown as Iəll or Ill. These sounds can be spelled
with the pattern **le**, **el**, or **al**.

Iəll or Ill   tremb**le**   jew**el**   usu**al**

Write the pattern that completes each Spelling Word
inside the school of fish. Then write each Spelling Word
in the box with the matching final sounds.

Spelling Words

1. tremble
2. battle
3. weapon
4. usual
5. reason
6. jewel
7. hidden
8. several
9. lessen
10. tunnel

My Study List
What other words do
you need to study for
spelling? Add them to My Study List
for *Island of the Blue Dolphins* in
the back of this book.

1 usu_____
2 hidd_____
3 tremb_____
4 sever_____
5 less_____

6 weap_____
7 jew_____
8 bat_____
9 tunn_____
10 reas_____

Iəll or Ill

11 _____   14 _____
12 _____   15 _____
13 _____   16 _____

Iənl or Inl

17 _____   19 _____
18 _____   20 _____

Name

Spelling Spree

What Am I? Write the Spelling Word that fits each clue.

1 I am not many, but I'm more than two.

_____

2 I tell why. _____

3 I am what you do when you are afraid.

_____

4 I am not out of the ordinary. _____

5 I am what you might do to a load that is too heavy.

_____

6 I have a top, bottom, and sides, but no ends.

_____

Proofreading Circle the four misspelled Spelling Words in this newspaper article. Then write each word correctly.

GHALAS-AT DAILY NEWS

A ship landed in Coral Cove this week with several Aleuts on board. Their captain said the reason they came was to hunt sea otter. He offered to trade from their jewle and weppon chests for the otter hides. A village woman hiden in the bushes overheard our chief arguing with the captain. Some say there will be a battel!

7 _____

8 _____

9 _____

10 _____

Dolphin Dialogue Imagine that you could understand a conversation between two dolphins. What would they say to each other? On a separate piece of paper, write a conversation the dolphins might have. Use Spelling Words from the list.

Name

Details About Dolphins

RUN-ON SENTENCE
There are many kinds of dolphins they can weigh from one hundred pounds to several tons.

CORRECTION
There are many kinds of dolphins. **They** can weigh from one hundred pounds to several tons.

CORRECTION
There are many kinds of dolphins, **and** they can weigh from one hundred pounds to several tons.

Run-on Sentences
Rewrite each run-on sentence, using correct capitalization and end marks. Some run-ons can be corrected in more than one way. Some have three parts. Unscramble the boldface letter or letters in each sentence to answer the question.

1 Dolphins are small whales the **l**argest dolphins are **c**alled killer whales.

_____

_____

2 Dolphins have a layer of blubber under their **s**kin the blubber keeps them warm it acts as a storage place for food.

_____

_____

3 Many kinds of dolphins **s**tay near land others live in the **o**pen ocean.

_____

_____

4 Dolphins **h**ave lungs dolphin mothers feed their young with milk such features make them mammals.

_____

_____

5 Are dolphins different from porpoises some scientists think so **o**thers disagree.

_____

_____

What do dolphins travel in? They travel in ___ ___ ___ ___ ___ ___ ___.

Name
_____

Name That Animal!

Run-on Sentences

Rewrite each run-on sentence
correctly. Then solve the riddle.

whale

gull

sea otter

sea elephant

1 This animal has a tough skin
its nose is long this excellent
swimmer gets its name from
these unusual features tell what it is.

_____

_____

_____

_____

Riddle answer: _____

2 This sea animal is related to the weasel the creature almost never
leaves the water it even eats and sleeps there what can it be?

_____

_____

_____

_____

Riddle answer: _____

3 What is this animal it has long wings it is also a good
swimmer it often swoops down over the water for food.

_____

_____

_____

_____

Riddle answer: _____

Let Me Tell You About the Time I . . .

Name

Do these topics give you any ideas?

Topics for Personal Narratives

▲ My happiest day
▲ A day on the river
▲ The time I got lost
▲ Learning to play a sport
▲ The time I fooled my brother/sister
▲ My mixed-up day
▲ Having my tonsils out
▲ My most frightening experience

My Personal Narrative Topics
Write five experiences you have had that you would like to write about.

_____

_____

_____

_____

_____

Ask yourself these questions about each idea you wrote.

Can I remember what happened in detail?

Would I enjoy writing about this?

Would this experience interest my audience?

Would part of this experience make a better story?

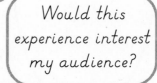

Now circle the topic you want to write about.

Name

Remember What Happened

Think about the important people, places, actions, and objects in your story. Draw them and list words that describe how each one looked, sounded, felt, smelled, or tasted. Then write the emotions you felt.

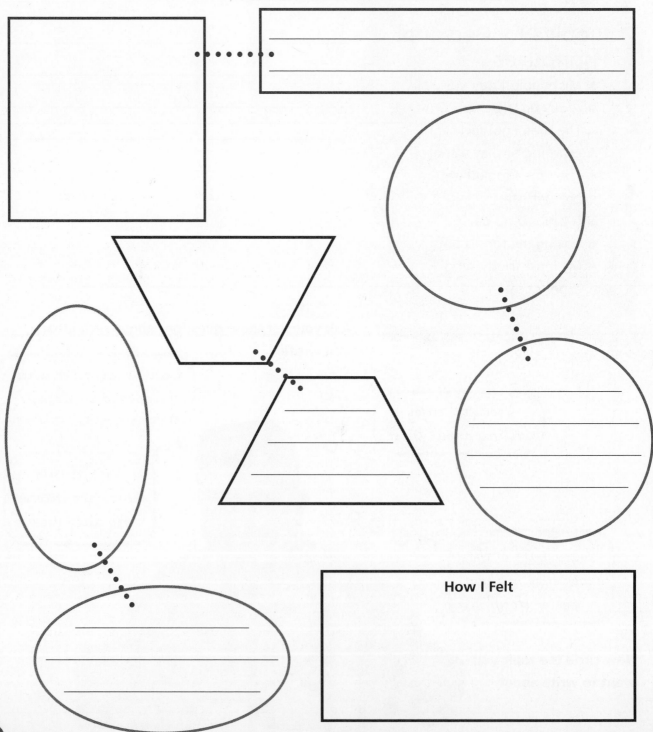

How I Felt

Name _____

Take Another Look

Reread and revise your personal narrative, using the Revising Checklist. Then use the Questions for a Writing Conference to discuss your story with a partner.

• Revising Checklist •

☐ Does the beginning set up the story and draw in the reader?

☐ Is the order of events clear?

☐ Did I give details about what I saw, heard, smelled, tasted, and touched?

☐ Did I use dialogue to bring the people and events to life?

☐ Did I tell how I felt?

Questions for a Writing Conference

• What do you like about this story?
• Is the beginning attention-getting? How could it be improved?
• Are any parts unclear? If so, what changes might make them clearer?
• Which details really make the story come alive? Which ones could be improved?
• Where could dialogue be added? taken out?

Write notes to help you remember ideas from your writing conference.

NOTES

_____

_____

_____

_____

_____

_____

_____

_____

....
Name

What's Missing?

Words are missing in the sentences. Fill in the blanks with a vocabulary word. Then circle the correct letters in the words and write the letters to answer the question.

1 Jaywalking in a city can be _____.

Directions: Circle the second letter.

2 Between the two houses, a tall hedge created a natural _____.

Directions: Circle the fifth letter.

3 The black line on the map shows the _____ between the two countries.

Directions: Circle the fifth letter.

4 The young woman had several housing _____ : an apartment alone, a shared apartment, a rooming house, or a college dormitory.

Directions: Circle the second, sixth, and ninth letters.

5 The sign said Welcome, but my _____ told me not to go in.

Directions: Circle the ninth letter.

What is Maniac missing?

_____ _____ _____ _____ _____ _____ _____

Name

"Here's What / Think..."

What do the other characters think of Maniac? Fill in the balloons with comments they might make. Use specific examples from the story.

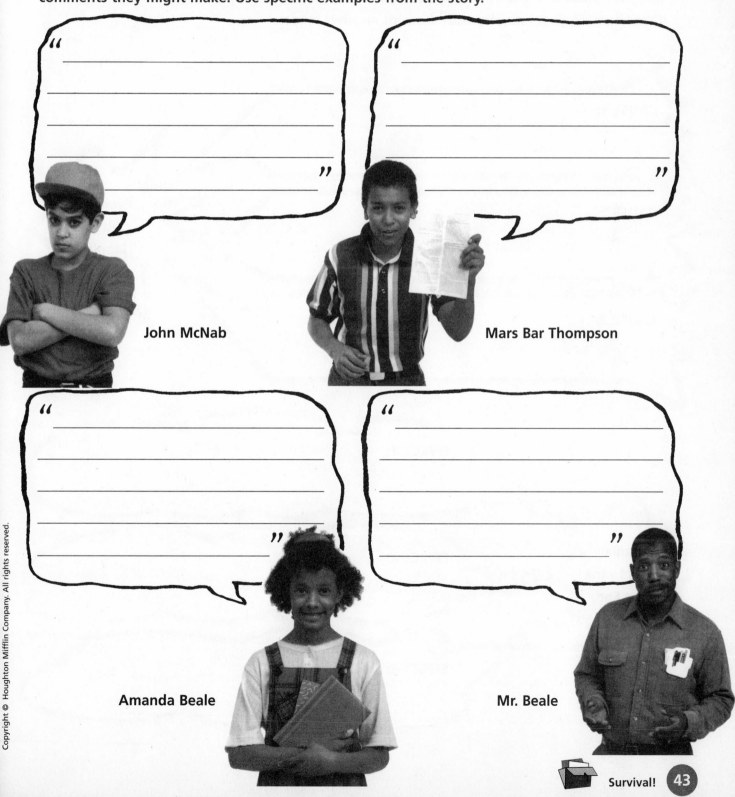

"_____
_____
_____
_____"

"_____
_____
_____
_____"

John McNab

Mars Bar Thompson

"_____
_____
_____
_____"

"_____
_____
_____
_____"

Amanda Beale

Mr. Beale

Survival! **43**

....

Name

BeCAUSE It's EFFECTive

Causes can have several effects. Effects can have several causes. You can prove this with these examples from *Maniac Magee.* Complete the graphic organizers. Then compare your answers with those of another reader.

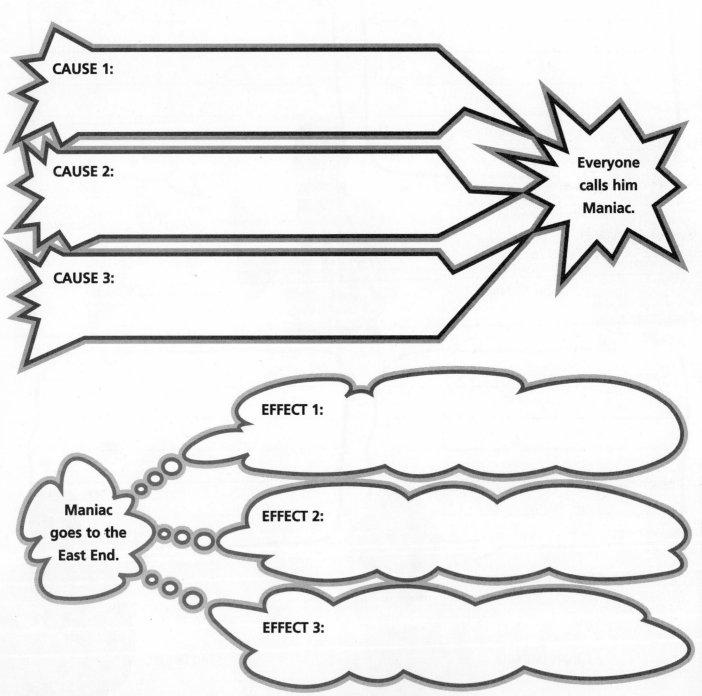

CAUSE 1:

CAUSE 2:

CAUSE 3:

Everyone calls him Maniac.

EFFECT 1:

EFFECT 2:

Maniac goes to the East End.

EFFECT 3:

Lights! Camera! Action!

**Read this paragraph. Then adapt it to a scene for a screenplay.
The format has been started for you. Use a separate piece of paper if
you need more room. When you finish, read your scene aloud with
another classmate.**

The boy held out his hand and asked for money. Carla didn't
know what to do. She'd never had a stranger ask her for money
before. Carla asked him his name. The boy smiled and said his
name was Sam. They talked for a few minutes about how cold and
wet the weather had been and how crowded the streets were this
time of year. Carla reached in her pocket for the fifty cents her
mother had given her to buy a newspaper. Before she dropped it
into his hand, Sam offered a piece of gum in exchange. It was
her favorite kind.

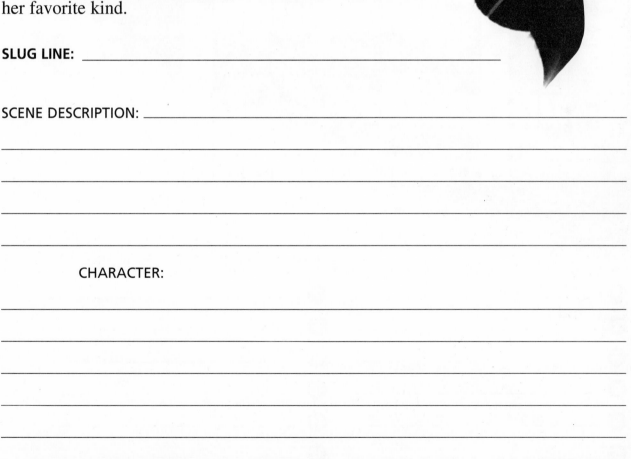

SLUG LINE: _____

SCENE DESCRIPTION: _____

_____

_____

_____

_____

CHARACTER:

_____

_____

_____

_____

_____

....
Name

Suffering Suffixes!

This puzzle is missing its clues! Write a clue for each word in the puzzle,
keeping in mind the meaning of the suffix as you write.

					7h						
8t		9l		1p	e	a	c	e	f	u	l
10b			e		a					
r	h	r	a	r					
e	11b	e	2e	f	f	o	r	t	l	e	s	s
a	e	a	a	l	t		
t	a	t	l	l		
3h	a	t	l	e	s	s	e	
l	i	n	4s	e	n	s	e	l	e	s	s	12s
e	f	i		i	
s	u	n		m	
s	5l	i	g	h	t	l	y	p	
	g		l	
	y	6s	i	n	c	e	r	e	l	y

Across

1 _____

2 _____

3 _____

4 _____

5 _____

6 _____

Down

7 _____

8 _____

9 _____

10 _____

11 _____

12 _____

46 Survival!

Name

Timely Titles

**Imagine that these titles are on Amanda's bookshelf.
Write a title to answer each question.**

Books on shelf: LYLE, LYLE, CROCODILE · INSTINKED · THE BLINK INSTINCT · THE FLOUNDERY BOUNDARY · AN URBAN SURVIVAL HANDBOOK · PROSPEROUS PROSPECTS · THE FATAL LADLE · THE DRAINIAC MANIAC

1 Which book describes the imaginary line between two fish?

_____

2 Which book describes a crime committed with a soup spoon?

_____

3 Which book tells the story of a wild, crazy plumber?

_____

4 Which book does Maniac read to the twins?

_____

5 Which book shows how skunks use their scents without having to be taught?

_____

6 Which book shows how to make lots of money—maybe?

_____

7 Which book will explain how to survive in a city?

_____

8 Which book explains how eyes naturally close when danger is near?

_____

Name

East Side, West Side

Homophones Each Spelling Word is a
homophone. Homophones are words that sound alike
but have different spellings and meanings.

WORD	SOUND	MEANING
threw	lthrool	flung
through	lthrool	among or between

Spelling Words

1. threw
2. through
3. hall
4. haul
5. stare
6. stair
7. heard
8. herd
9. waste
10. waist

My Study List
What other words do
you need to study for
spelling? Add them to My Study List
for Maniac Magee in the back of this
book.

Help the East Side and the West Side get together.
Write the Spelling Word that matches each meaning.
Then draw lines across Hector Street to connect the
homophone pairs.

WEST SIDE

1 _____ to spend or
use foolishly

2 _____ to gather or
flock together

3 _____ to look with
a steady gaze

4 _____ among or
between

5 _____ to move from
one place to
another

EAST SIDE

a flight of
steps 6 _____

a corridor 7 _____

flung 8 _____

a body part
between the 9 _____
ribs and hips

sensed sounds
through the ear 10 _____

Name

Spelling Spree

Proofreading Circle the four misspelled Spelling Words in this diary entry. Then write each word correctly.

> Dear Diary,
> Well, today was filled with adventures! First, I got chased by a herd of Cobras and had to hawl across town lickety-split. Then I ran into a guy I'd herred of, Mars Bar Thompson. Boy, did he give me a mean stayre! I was in big trouble until Amanda came along. The fit she throo saved me from Mars Bar's gang!

Spelling Words

1. threw
2. through
3. hall
4. haul
5. stare
6. stair
7. heard
8. herd
9. waste
10. waist

1 _____

2 _____

3 _____

4 _____

How Not to Be "Bad" Circle the Spelling Word that makes sense in each sentence on Maniac's list. Then write the correct homophone.

Things to Do for the Beales

5 Each day, hug Mrs. Beale around the waste/waist to thank her for my new address.

6 Vacuum the hall/haul every few days.

7 Once a day, heard/herd Bow Wow, Hester, and Lester outside to play.

8 Go threw/through the house each day and pick up toys.

9 Dust the stare/stair once a week.

10 Don't waste/waist any food at dinner.

5 _____

6 _____

7 _____

8 _____

9 _____

10 _____

Change of Address On a separate piece of paper, write a postcard that Maniac might write to a friend. Share the news of Maniac's new address and any other news he might have. Use Spelling Words from the list.

The Bases Are Loaded!

Using Commas Correctly

A cartoonist has drawn a comic strip using Maniac, Amanda, and Hank as characters. Place commas where they belong. Then draw your own cartoon below and write three sentences to go with it. Use commas in a series, with an introductory word, and with a name in direct address.

The ball flies off the bat, into the air, and over the fence.
Yes, it is a home run!
You did it, Maniac!

1

Maniac I have a question for you.

Well I'm sure I can answer it Amanda.

2

Does it take longest to run from first to second base from second to third base or from third to home?

Give me time to check a baseball almanac to talk to the coach and to measure the field.

3

I know the answer Maniac.

Oh be quiet and let me think Hank.

It takes longest Maniac to run from second to third.

4

All right Hank how do you know?

Well there is a shortstop in the middle!

....

Name

Directions, Please!

Using Commas Correctly Help Joshua ask Alicia
for directions from the school to the railroad station. Write
a sentence in each speech balloon to tell what the character
is saying. Include an introductory word and a person's
name in direct address in your sentences.

_____

_____

_____

_____

_____

_____

_____

_____

Now look at the map, and write
directions for **Joshua** to follow from
the school to the railroad station.
Use words in a series, introductory
words, and a person's name in direct
address in your sentences.

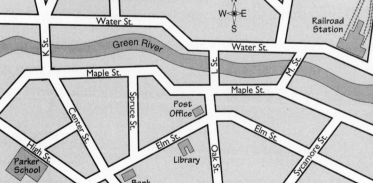

_____

_____

_____

_____

_____

_____

_____

_____

_____

Name

And the Winner Is . . .

Think about which character in the theme most deserves an award for her or his outstanding ability to survive an extreme situation. Fill out the chart to help you plan your award.

The character I think deserves the Survival Award is:

_____

Write the events that put your character in an extreme and threatening situation.	Write the actions that your character took to survive the events from column 1.

Present your award to the class. Use the checklist to be sure you are ready to make your presentation.

 LIST

❑ My award explains how my character survived an extreme situation.
❑ My award describes the events of my character's situation in order.
❑ I can explain why I think my character deserves to win a Survival Award.

Design an award that explains how your character survived extreme conditions. Point out how your character's actions helped your character survive the situation. Write the events on your award in sequential order.

Name

In Search of the Real Me

The characters in these selections embark on a kind of search in which they learn more about themselves. Compare and contrast their searches—and what they find—by completing the chart.

	The No-Guitar Blues	Last Summer with Maizon
What challenge does the main character face?		
What choice does the main character make?		
Does the main character make the right choice? Why or why not?		
How does the main character change?		

Name

In Search of the Real Me

The characters in these selections embark on a kind of search in which they learn more about themselves. Compare and contrast their searches—and what they find—by completing the chart.

	The Scholarship Jacket	The Star Fisher
What challenge does the main character face?		
What choice does the main character make?		
Does the main character make the right choice? Why or why not?		
How does the main character change?		

Name _____

Vocabulary Blues

Fill in the appropriate words in this verse of a blues song.
Then write two more verses using the other four words.

| fidgeted | deceitful | wrongdoing | mimicked | confident | privacy |

VERSE 1

My baby came to me this morning

Interrupted my _____.

I _____ when I saw her,

And said, "What do you want with me?"

CHORUS

I got the blues
Those red-hot vocabulary blues
Whenever I feel nerdy
I try to sound real wordy
I got the vocabulary blues.

VERSE 2

VERSE 3

Name

Explain the Chain

Pretend you are Fausto. Fill in the spaces to explain the chain of events in *The No-Guitar Blues.*

I needed money because . . .

But . . .

So first I tried . . .

But that didn't work because . . .

Then I found a _____ and developed a great plan:

The plan worked, but I felt guilty because . . .

So I decided to . . .

That made me feel better.

Things worked out okay because . . .

Name

In Search of a Few Clues

Does Gary Soto want his readers to predict that Fausto will learn to play the guitar? Find clues in the story—and in your own experience—that lead you to this prediction. When you note a clue from the selection, include the page number where you found it.

PREDICTION: Fausto will learn to play the guitar.

Character Clues	Story Events	Personal Experience

Name _____

Astounding Appositives

Use a word or group of words as an appositive as
you write Fausto's answers to his friend.

1 **Friend:** Hey, Fausto, when was the last time you saw your favorite band?

Fausto: _____

_____

2 **Friend:** What did you find that you tried to get a reward for?

Fausto: _____

_____

_____

3 **Friend:** Who were the rich people you met?

Fausto: _____

_____

_____

4 **Friend:** What did you see at their house that you remember?

Fausto: _____

_____

5 **Friend:** What did they give you besides a reward?

Fausto: _____

_____

_____

6 **Friend:** What did your grandfather give you?

Fausto: _____

_____

Name

Deadline: Apostrophes!

You're a newspaper editor. Your top reporter has just handed you a story about a lost dog. The story is perfect except for one detail: the apostrophe key on her typewriter was broken! Underline each word that needs an apostrophe and insert the punctuation, as the example in the title shows.

<u>DOG'S</u> OWNERS OFFER REWARD

by I. Ken Spell

On Monday morning, Virginia and Harold Whites neighborhood was plastered with fliers announcing the disappearance of their dog, Lucky. Luckys coat is golden. Hes a medium-sized dog, weighing about 40 pounds. Luckys collar is red, and hes wearing a dog tag that shows his owners address. "Were so worried," Mrs. White said in Mondays interview. "If anyone sees him, dont hesitate to call us." The Whites phone number is 555-LOST.

Name

Tagging the Dog

Why do these dogs have such strange names? Fill in each dog tag with a sentence that explains the meaning of its name.

Example: REVEALING

This dog likes to make things known.

MIMICKED

AUTHENTIC

CONFIDENT

DECEITFUL

FIDGETED

FAULTLESS

WRONGDOING

OBVIOUS

PRIVACY

Name _____

Word Repair

Compound Words
Each Spelling Word is a **compound word**. A compound word is made up of two or more smaller words. A compound word may be written as one word, as a hyphenated word, or as separate words.

teenager   old-fashioned   living room

Spelling Words

1. teenager
2. freeway
3. secondhand
4. living room
5. wrongdoing
6. wallpaper
7. dog tag
8. warehouse
9. old-fashioned
10. brother-in-law

My Study List
What other words do you need to study for spelling? Add them to My Study List for *The No-Guitar Blues* in the back of this book.

Write the missing part or parts of the Spelling Word on each slip of paper. Then write each compound word on the guitar with the correct heading.

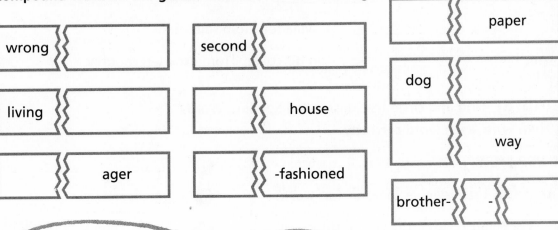

wrong }   second }

living }   } house

        } ager   } -fashioned

        } paper

dog }

        } way

brother- }   -

One-Word Compounds

1 _____
2 _____
3 _____
4 _____
5 _____
6 _____

Compounds with Hyphens

7 _____
8 _____

Compounds with Separate Words

9 _____
10 _____

Name

Spelling Spree

Swifties Tom Swift was a book character who always spoke in a clever way. Everything he said was somehow related to how he said it. Write the Spelling Word that completes each Swiftie.

Example: "I'll turn on the light," Tom said brightly.

1 "If I take the _____, I'll get stuck in a traffic jam," Tom said haltingly.

2 "My _____ treats my sister like a queen," Tom said majestically.

3 "Don't accuse me of any _____!" Tom said guiltily.

4 "My, what a lovely, _____ village!" Tom said quaintly.

5 "Put Rover's new _____ on his collar," Tom growled roughly.

Proofreading Find and circle five misspelled Spelling Words in this ad. Then write each word correctly.

STUDENT FOR HIRE!

Student, almost a teanager, is looking for work.

Is your livving room dingy? Do you want your

kitchen to look old-fashioned? I can paint or put

up wall paper. I can mow your lawn or clean

your warehuse. Will work for money or for a

second-hand guitar. Call Fausto at 555-1986.

6 _____

7 _____

8 _____

9 _____

10 _____

Rock and Roll Words Fausto loved the rock group Los Lobos. Imagine that you are a songwriter for Los Lobos. On a separate sheet of paper, write the words for a song the band might sing. Use Spelling Words from the list.

Name

Musical Notes

"I think Los Lobos is a really great band!" said Lance.
Inez asked, "How can you like Los Lobos and the Rolling Stones too?"
"Well," Lance replied, "it's not hard. They both have great songs."
"That's true," said Inez. "They're very different, though."

Punctuating Dialogue Here are notes for a magazine
article from an interview with Nicki Dash, guitar player with the band
Electric Eels. Rewrite each note, using correct capitalization and punctuation.

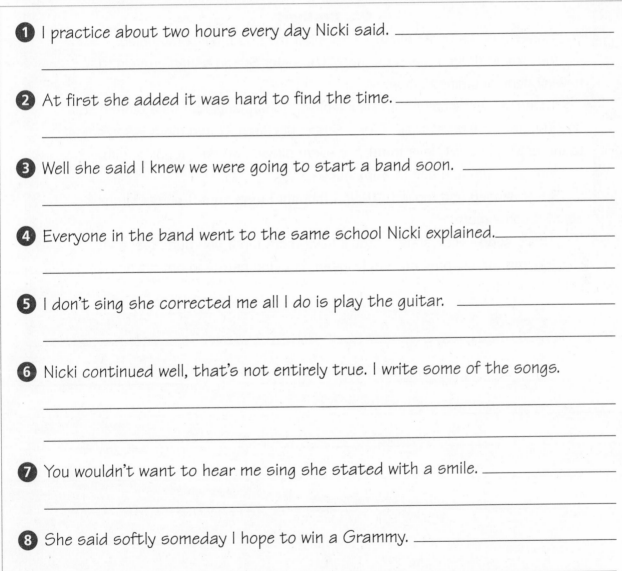

1 I practice about two hours every day Nicki said. _____

_____

2 At first she added it was hard to find the time. _____

_____

3 Well she said I knew we were going to start a band soon. _____

_____

4 Everyone in the band went to the same school Nicki explained._____

_____

5 I don't sing she corrected me all I do is play the guitar. _____

_____

6 Nicki continued well, that's not entirely true. I write some of the songs.

_____

_____

7 You wouldn't want to hear me sing she stated with a smile. _____

_____

8 She said softly someday I hope to win a Grammy. _____

_____

Name

To Tell the Truth

Punctuating Dialogue You have started a story to submit to *Kidpower* magazine. Continue the story by writing a follow-up dialogue between Susan and her mother. Use correct capitalization and punctuation and begin a new paragraph with each change in speaker.

Oh, Brother!

"Honesty is the best policy. That's what they say," Alex mumbled.

"Hey, what do you mean by that?" his sister Susan asked crossly. "I haven't done anything dishonest."

"When you tell a half-truth," Alex replied, "what happens to the other half?"

"This isn't a federal case, Alex," Susan declared. "I told Mom I was going to the movies. I don't have to tell her every single person I'm going with."

"Are you sure you don't?" Alex asked.

Susan sighed and replied, "Well, I thought I was sure. I guess I'll think about it some more."

"That's good," Alex stated. "You'll have more fun if you don't feel guilty."

"Always the big brother," said Susan, shaking her head but smiling as she walked away.

○ ○ ○

_____

_____

_____

_____

_____

_____

_____

Edit Credit

Imagine that you are making notes to edit a thesaurus.
Place each vocabulary word in the correct entry space so
that it is paired with a synonym and an antonym.

| distracted | relieve | somberly | desolate |

Entry

THESAURUS

	Synonyms	Antonyms
1 _____	free up	intensify
2 _____	gloomily, darkly	happily
3 _____	lonely, empty	crowded
4 _____	confused	focused

Write one sentence that illustrates the meaning of each of the vocabulary words.

5 _____

_____

6 _____

_____

7 _____

_____

8 _____

_____

Name

All A-Board!

Imagine that *Last Summer with Maizon* is being made into a TV after-school special. Complete the storyboards to describe four scenes in the story.

1 WHO: _____

WHERE: at Penn Station
WHAT HAPPENS: _____
_____
_____
_____

2 WHO: _____

WHERE: Margaret's classroom
WHAT HAPPENS: _____
_____
_____
_____

3 WHO: _____

WHERE: the same classroom, the next day
WHAT HAPPENS: _____
_____
_____
_____

4 WHO: _____

WHERE: on the stoop of Margaret's house
WHAT HAPPENS: _____
_____
_____
_____

Name

Be a Story Detective

Choose three inferences from the list that are appropriate for
Last Summer with Maizon. Write them on the chart. Then use
story clues and your own knowledge to support your choices.

1. Margaret is a sensitive person and a talented poet.
2. Maizon is a funny person.
3. Hattie is a very wise and talented woman.
4. Hattie and Ms. Dell are like a second family for Margaret.
5. Margaret does not miss her father.

Inference	Story Clues	Personal Knowledge

Name

Poem Planner

Use the organizer below to help you plan your poem.

Name the feeling, name the care, · · · · · · · · ·

The time, the place, who else was there. · · · · · ·

Name the sights, the smells, the sounds,
and other things that were around. · · · · · · · ·

Now tell what images you find
that bring this feeling back to mind. · · · · · · · ·

A metaphor or simile
could explain these things to me. · · · · · · · · · ·

Will your words rhyme, or have a beat?
Or do you like things not so neat? · · · · · · ·

Will your lines make a tidy stack?
Or walk   the   page
                        to here · · · · · ·
        and back?

Compound Interest

Four words make up these compound words: *loose-leaf* and *notebook*. When you read about Maizon drumming her fingers against a windowpane, did you notice that *windowpane* was a compound word? Write more compound words using these words.

Play this compound word game. Start with one compound word. Use one of the words in it to form a new compound word. Then form a new compound with part of the new word. Keep going as long as you can. Write down your word chain.

Example: classroom ➔ roommate ➔ schoolmate ➔ high school ➔ high-speed ➔ speedboat ➔ steamboat ➔ steamroller

_____

_____

_____

_____

_____

_____

_____

Name

Last Letter from Maizon

Margaret has finally received a letter from Maizon! (Actually, you're going to write it.) Use the words to describe what being away is like.

bleak	somberly	distracted	deserted	sighed
concentrate	desolate	encourage	relieve	uncertain

Dear Margaret,

_____

_____

_____

_____

_____

_____

_____

_____

_____

_____

_____

_____

_____

_____

_____

Sincerely,

Maizon

Name

Front-Stoop Syllables

The VCCV and VCCCV Patterns

Each two-syllable Spelling Word has the vowel-consonant-consonant-vowel (**VCCV**) pattern or the vowel-consonant-consonant-consonant-vowel (**VCCCV**) pattern.

Divide most **VCCV** words into syllables between the consonants. In both patterns, when two consonants make one sound, as in *trophy,* or form a cluster, as in *empty,* divide the words into syllables before or after those two consonants. In each syllable, look for familiar spelling patterns you have learned, and spell the word by syllables.

Spelling Words

1. empty
2. absent
3. whisper
4. laughter
5. instead
6. surround
7. applaud
8. trophy
9. swallow
10. snicker

My Study List
What other words do you need to study for spelling? Add them to My Study List for *Last Summer with Maizon* in the back of this book.

VC | CV	VCC | V	V | CCV	VC | CCV	VCC | CV
ab | sent	snick | er	tro | phy	in | stead	emp | ty

Draw a line to connect the syllables of each Spelling Word. Then write each Spelling Word below the correct syllable pattern. Draw a line between the syllables.

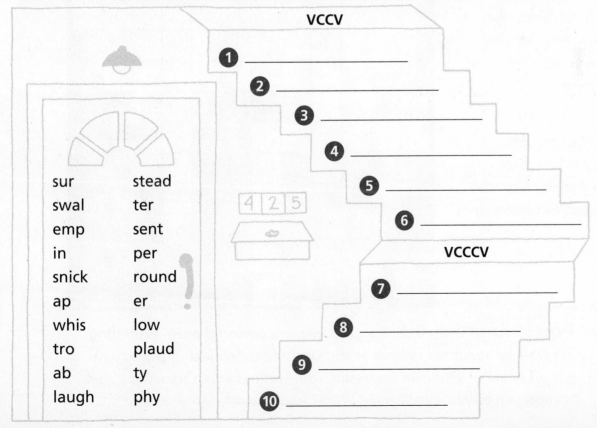

VCCV

1 _____
2 _____
3 _____
4 _____
5 _____
6 _____

VCCCV

7 _____
8 _____
9 _____
10 _____

sur   stead
swal   ter
emp   sent
in   per
snick round
ap   er
whis   low
tro   plaud
ab   ty
laugh phy

Name _____

Spelling Spree

Proofreading Find and circle the four misspelled
Spelling Words in this beginning of an essay. Then
write each word correctly.

My Summer Vacation

When school let out, I faced an emty summer. Should I join a swim club and
shoot for a trophy? Or should I try out for summer theater insted? I decided to
swalow my fear and try out for a role in a play. Amazingly, in spite of my sister's
loud snikker at the audition, I got the role.

1 _____

2 _____

3 _____

4 _____

Crossword Puzzle Write the Spelling Word that fits each clue.

Across

2. to express enjoyment or
   approval by clapping
4. to be on all sides of
5. not present

Down

1. to speak very softly
3. response to a joke
6. prize given as a symbol
   of victory or achievement

 Poetic Expressions Margaret wrote a powerful poem expressing
her feelings about her father's death. On a separate sheet of paper, write
a short poem of your own expressing your feelings about something that
is important to you. Use Spelling Words from the list.

Name

Prize Words

Nouns and Abbreviations
Proofread the poetry prize announcement, using proofreading marks from the box. Use abbreviations wherever possible in the address.

Common Noun	Proper Noun	Abbreviation
company	The Becker Company	The Becker Co.
address	69 Madison Street	69 Madison St.

Proofreading Marks

∧	Add
⊙	Add a period.
℘	Take out
≡	Capitalize
/	Make a small letter.

The Brooklyn arts society

Giovanni prize for young Poets

All Participants must be between ten and fifteen years of age. Send three copies of your Poem and a stamped, self-addressed Envelope to

Mister Mario Mello

Mount Ryan school

75 channel avenue

brooklyn, New York 11201

On a separate sheet of paper, rewrite the announcement correctly.

Name

Subway Sales Pitches

Nouns and Abbreviations Write subway ads for these items: a TV on a watchband, a state T-shirt, and a special unicycle. Use common nouns, proper nouns, and abbreviations. Make up a name for each item, write a brief description to help sell it, and make up a name and address for the place where it can be bought.

Name

I Resign

Sometimes standing up for what you value means putting yourself at risk. Imagine you are a teacher who has seen a student treated unfairly. Draft a letter to the principal in which you use all the vocabulary words.

| resign | dignity | despaired | tradition | significance | dismay |

Dear Ms. Ziegler:

_____

_____

_____

_____

_____

_____

_____

_____

_____

Sincerely,

_____

_____ Department

Name

Who Gets the Jacket?

Who should get the scholarship jacket? Why? Fill in the answers according to each character's point of view.

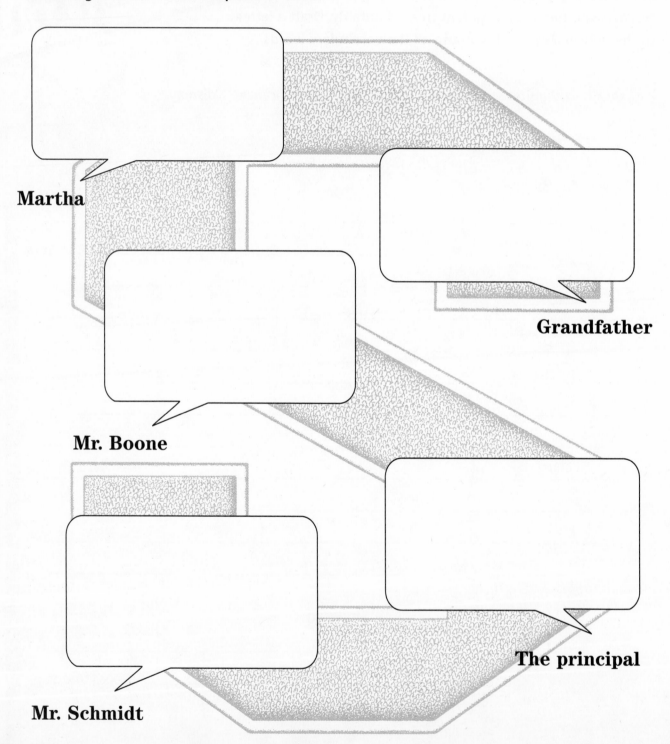

Martha

Grandfather

Mr. Boone

Mr. Schmidt

The principal

Name

Use the Clues

The word *therefore* often signals that a conclusion is coming.
Use the clues in the sentences to draw conclusions that begin
with *therefore*. Compare your sentences with a partner's.

1 The school awards a scholarship jacket for the student with the highest grades over eight years. Martha has earned all A's since the first grade.

Therefore

2 Martha overheard her teachers arguing about her. The principal summoned her, looking uncomfortable.

Therefore

3 Martha told her grandfather's words to the principal. The principal changed his mind.

Therefore

4 Martha had been home from school for an hour. Her hands were as dirty as her grandfather's.

Therefore

In Search of the Real Me **77**

By the Book

Choose a book you have enjoyed to be the subject for a book report. Answer
the questions to help you recall information and clarify your opinions. Use
your notes to write a complete book report on a separate sheet of paper.

Title of Book _____

Author _____

Introduction

• Is the book fiction or nonfiction? _____

• What details will catch your reader's attention?

_____

_____

Body

• Who are the characters? _____

_____

• What are some details about setting and plot? _____

_____

_____

• What are some of the problems that the characters face? _____

_____

_____

Conclusion

• Did you like the book? Why or why not? _____

_____

_____

• What hint can you give about the ending? _____

_____

_____

Root It Out

Use the word grids to put together words with the roots *dict* and *aud*.
To build words, move from square to square, adding syllables as you go.
Write each word before its meaning. Use a dictionary if necessary.

ion	contra	e
bene	DICT	pre
able	juris	ver

1 _____ : legal control over something

2 _____ : to tell what will happen in the future

3 _____ : a statement of future events

4 _____ : an opposite statement

5 _____ : a decision reached by a jury

6 _____ : an order or decree by someone in power

7 _____ : capable of being foreseen

8 _____ : a blessing or wish for goodness

in	ience	meter
ory	AUD	io
it	ion	ible

9 _____ : loud enough to be heard

10 _____ : not loud enough to be heard

11 _____ : a check or hearing about financial records

12 _____ : having to do with hearing

13 _____ : a tryout, especially in music or theater

14 _____ : related to the recording or broadcasting of sound

15 _____ : people who gather to listen or watch

16 _____ : a device that measures a person's sense of hearing

In Search of the Real Me   79

Name _____

Pocket Pairs

Pair these words—two to a pocket—by matching those with similar meanings. Then write the meanings on the pocket labels.

dismay	despaired	meaningful	tradition	significance	custom
pride	withdraw	horror	gave up	dignity	resign

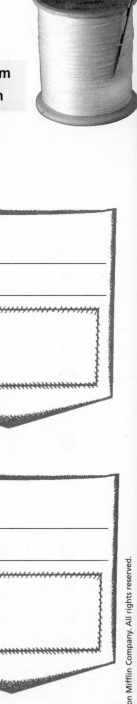

3 _____ jacket _____

_____ parka _____

types of coats

1 _____

_____

6 _____

_____

4 _____

_____

2 _____

_____

7 _____

_____

5 _____

_____

Bean Field Search

The VCV Pattern
Each two-syllable Spelling Word has the **vowel-consonant-vowel (VCV)** pattern. Divide a **VCV** word into syllables before or after the consonant. If the first syllable has the short vowel sound, divide the word after the consonant. If the first syllable is unstressed or has a long vowel sound, divide the word before the consonant.

Spelling Words

1. award
2. eager
3. refuse
4. minute
5. avoid
6. labor
7. fever
8. body
9. promise
10. panic

My Study List
What other words do you need to study for spelling? Add them to My Study List for "The Scholarship Jacket" in the back of this book.

```
V C | V              V | C V

m i n | u t e  |min´it|   a | w a r d   |ə wôrd´|
                          e a | g e r   |e´gər|
```

The two syllables of a Spelling Word are hidden in each horizontal row. A bean plant separates the syllables. Circle the two syllables in each row. Then write the Spelling Words under the correct patterns.

```
      m a   x f e   v e r c i
e a   g e r t   p r l     w
      q u a     v o i d y a b   BEANS
p a b   m i   p a n   i c
m m i n   u t e r e     o   e r
    t w r e   f u s e u   x i
b e k l     b o d     y j w
r l a   w a r d z p     r m
u n   w a p r o m   i s e l
    t l a   b o r   c m i o
```

V | C V
1. _____
2. _____
3. _____
4. _____
5. _____
6. _____

V C | V
8. _____
8. _____
9. _____
10. _____

Name _____

Spelling Spree

Proofreading Circle the five misspelled Spelling Words in this speech. Then write each word correctly.

For those of us who are graduating, the future holds much promice. We are eeger to move on to high school and college. With mind and boddy, we will then spend every minute building a new world. Wherever we laber—in factories or offices, on roads or farms—we will be making a difference. This is our destiny, one we cannot refeuse.

1 _____   **3** _____   **5** _____

2 _____   **4** _____

Word Switch Write a Spelling Word to replace each underlined definition in the sentences. Write your words on the scholarship jacket.

6. To whom will you <u>give for outstanding performance</u> the scholarship jacket?

7. I began to <u>experience a feeling of great fear</u> when I realized I had to give a speech.

8. If you have a <u>high body temperature</u>, don't go to school.

9. Please don't try to <u>keep away from</u> me.

10. Please come to my office when you have a <u>unit of time equal to sixty seconds</u>.

6 _____
7 _____
8 _____
9 _____
10 _____

Opinion Buttons Martha finally got her scholarship jacket. But what if Joann were given the jacket? How would you feel? On a separate sheet of paper, write a few slogans for buttons showing your opinion. Use Spelling Words from the list.

Name

Word Play

Singular and Plural Nouns

Write the singular or plural form of
the nouns below to complete each
sentence. Then unscramble the circled
letters to find an important word
from "The Scholarship Jacket."

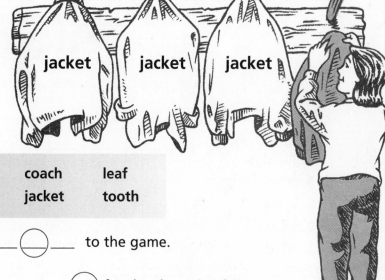

child	bus	school	coach	leaf
day	hero	family	jacket	tooth

1 The teammates rode in two __ __ __ ◯ __ to the game.

2 They were playing another __ __ __ __ __ ◯ for the championship.

3 Each team had two __ ◯ __ ◯ __ __ __ .

4 Each player wore a team __ __ ◯ __ __ __ __ .

5 Would the players be __ __ ◯ __ __ __ today?

6 Many young __ __ ◯ __ ◯ __ __ ◯ from the school were watching the game.

7 They sat and cheered with their __ __ __ __ ◯ __ __ __ __ .

8 A sudden fierce wind blew some __ __ __ ◯ __ __ onto the field.

9 The onlookers' __ __ __ ◯ __ began to chatter in the cold.

10 Every __ ◯ __ the autumn weather was growing colder.

Question: Who is at the top of the class?

Answer: the __ __ __ __ __ __ __ __

A Classy Puzzle

Singular and Plural Nouns   Complete the puzzle with the plural form of each noun. Use a dictionary to check correct plural forms.

Across

1. valedictorian
2. holiday
5. scholarship
9. value
10. goose
11. child
12. solo
13. fox

Down

1. veto
3. deer
4. life
6. loyalty
7. success
8. dish

Use at least two puzzle nouns in the singular or plural form to write a motto for your class or school.

_____

_____

_____

Name

What a Great Idea!

Do these titles spark any story ideas?

A Strange Friendship

Caught in a Storm

TRIP TO XANTHORA

The Purple Palace

Lost!

THE FROG AND THE FISH

The Mall Mystery

Music, Music, Music

The Big Game

Moving Again

My Story Topics In each
~~book,~~ write an idea that you would
like to write a story about. Note the
kind of story each one would be,
such as a mystery or a tall tale.

Think about each idea you
wrote. Ask yourself these
questions.

Will it make an
interesting story?

Do I have enough
ideas for the plot?

Can I picture the
characters and
setting clearly?

Will I enjoy writing
about it?

**Now circle the topic you will
write about.**

Name _____

What's the Plan?

Complete the diagram to help you plan your story.

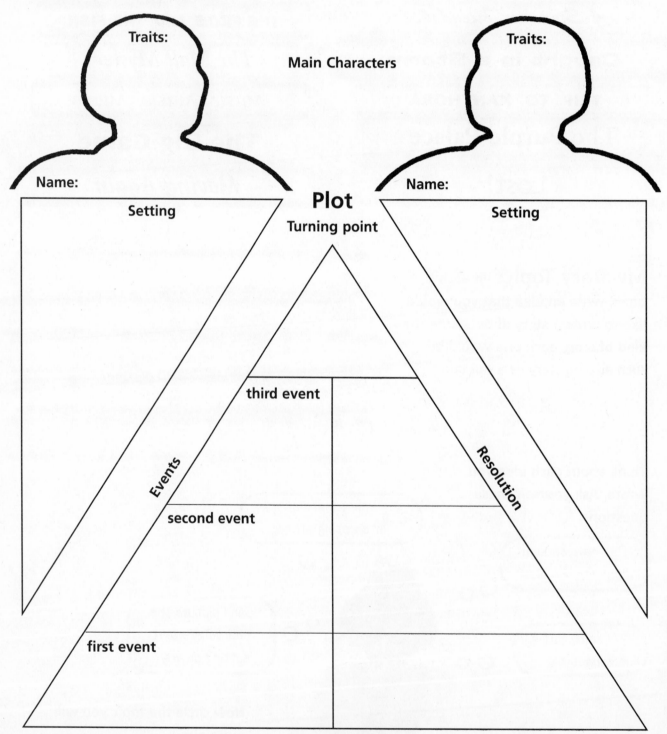

Traits:

Main Characters

Traits:

Name:

Name:

Setting

Setting

Plot
Turning point

third event

Events

Resolution

second event

first event

Problem: _____

Name

Make It Better

Reread and revise your story, using the Revising Checklist. Then use the Questions
for a Writing Conference to help you discuss your story with a classmate.

• Revising Checklist •

☐ Does the plot have a problem, a turning point, and a resolution?

☐ Have I used dialogue to show what the characters are like? to give information or to help tell what is happening?

☐ Have I used details to describe the characters, settings, and events?

☐ Does the ending finish the story in a way that makes sense?

Questions for a Writing Conference

• Does the story begin in an interesting way?

• Is the problem clear? Do all the events deal with that problem?

• What events or information is missing?

• Do the characters seem real? Does their dialogue fit their personalities?

• Could some parts of the story be told through dialogue? Should some dialogue be taken out?

• Does the ending fit the story and make it seem complete?

My Notes

Write notes to help you remember ideas discussed in your writing conference.

_____

_____

_____

_____

_____

_____

_____

Name _____

First-Day Feelings

Help Kim revise her essay about her first day in a new school. Replace the underlined phrases with vocabulary words. Then read the revised essay aloud. How does it sound with the new words included?

| humiliated | etiquette | cringed | estimation | ridicule |

The New School Blues

I was so upset at the thought of starting sixth grade in a new school that I slumped down in the front seat of the car and <u>kind of rolled up into a ball</u> _____ when we turned onto School Street. I decided I had better take hold of myself, so I straightened up, got out of the car, and marched to the front door of the school.

I had visited the school once before and knew where to go, so at least I wouldn't be <u>made to feel stupid</u> _____ by having to ask someone to show me the way. Although I hoped no one would make fun of my clothes, I was sure that I could handle some <u>teasing</u> _____ (but not too much).

Mom says that <u>proper behavior</u> _____ in and out of school requires me to be polite to everyone. In my <u>way of thinking about things</u> _____, this new school was going to be impossible, manners or no manners. Fortunately, by the end of the second week, I knew things wouldn't be as bad as I had feared.

Name

Six Pieces of Pie

Fill in the answers on each slice of pie.

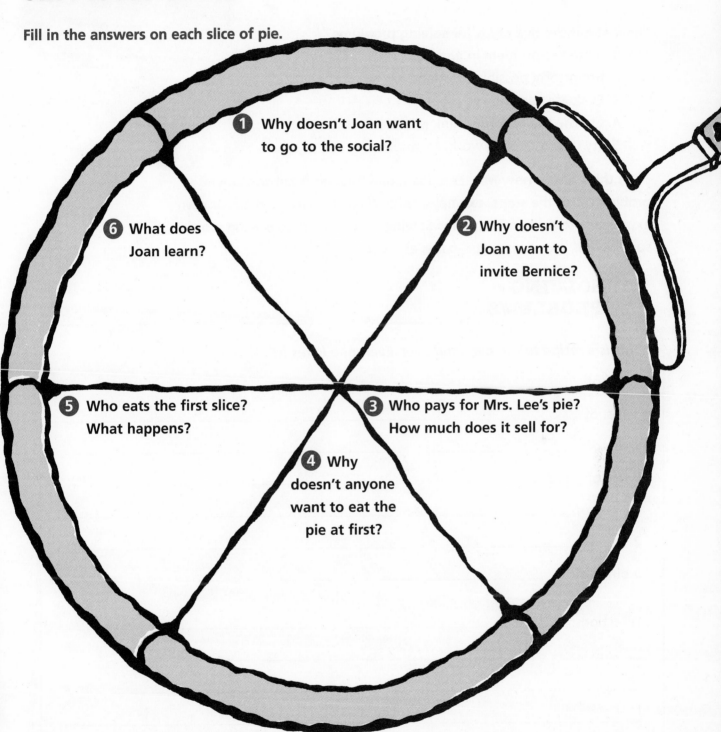

1 Why doesn't Joan want to go to the social?

6 What does Joan learn?

2 Why doesn't Joan want to invite Bernice?

5 Who eats the first slice? What happens?

3 Who pays for Mrs. Lee's pie? How much does it sell for?

4 Why doesn't anyone want to eat the pie at first?

Extra! Write a letter from Bernice to a friend she has met in her travels. Describe the events at the pie social from Bernice's point of view.

In Search of the Real Me **89**

A Recipe for Problem Solving

Think about the five steps for solving problems.

    1. State the problem in words.

    2. Brainstorm possible solutions.

    3. Evaluate each one.

    4. Choose the one you think is best.

    5. Try it. If it doesn't work, try another.

Then think about how Mrs. Lee, Joan, and Reverend Bobson solved problems. Use the steps, examples from *The Star Fisher*, and your own experience to write a Recipe for Solving Problems. Use cooking words such as *add*, *blend*, *mix*, *stir*, *bake*, and *eat*.

SOLVING PROBLEMS

This is a recipe to use over and over. Everyone loves it!

1 tsp. of _____

3 Tbs. of _____

1 cup of _____

2 tsp. of _____

1/2 cup of _____

2 Tbs. of _____

a pinch of _____

Directions: _____

_____

_____

_____

_____

_____
Name

Attention! Attend!

Write an announcement based on the information provided. Make the announcement interesting so that people will want to attend the event.

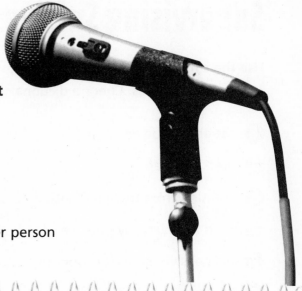

Who?   all middle school students
What?   a spring dance
When?   Friday, March 31, 7:00 P.M.
Where?   Lincoln Middle School gym
Why?   to support the local library fund: $2.00 per person
How?   dress casual; music provided by DJ

....

Name

Supervising Suffixes

Use the suffixes *-able, -ible, -ive, -ical, -ous* to make adjectives with the
following meanings. Check a dictionary, if necessary, for spelling.

1 not able to be destroyed   _____

2 like a disaster   _____

3 resulting from the imagination   _____

4 good for everyday practice   _____

5 inexpensive, good for economy   _____

6 full of joy   _____

7 appealing to logic   _____

8 able to be loved   _____

9 able to be eaten   _____

10 not able to be resisted   _____

You're an editor of a cooking gadgets catalog. You need to add a line to
the following text by adding adjectives. Use the words from the list above.

YOU'LL NEVER PEEL APPLES THE OLD WAY with this _____

invention. Just place an _____ apple into the _____

holder and turn the handle clockwise. The result will be an _____, perfect

apple, all ready for _____, _____ little mouths to

munch on and stay healthy. This _____ gadget will last a lifetime. It's the

only _____ solution to those _____ skinned knuckles.

This _____ tool can save you time and money. Order yours today!

Name

Miss Lee's Book

It's many years after the events of *The Star Fisher*, and Joan Lee has written a book about ways to welcome new people. Use three words to complete the title and the first two chapter titles. Write titles for the other chapters, using a word from the box in each one.

humiliated	polite
ridicule	etiquette
gratitude	courtesy
cringed	hospitality
estimation	thoughtfully

Miss Lee's Book of

Welcoming New People to Town

Table of Contents

Chapter 1: "I _____ When I Walked In!": First Reactions

Chapter 2: Making Sure New People Don't Feel _____

Chapter 3: _____

Chapter 4: _____

Chapter 5: _____

Chapter 6: _____

Chapter 7: _____

Chapter 8: _____

Chapter 9: _____

....

Name

Word Pies

Spelling the |sh| Sound Each Spelling Word
has the sound you hear at the beginning of **sheriff**,
shown as |sh|. The |sh| sound may be spelled with the
pattern **sh**, **ti**, **ci**, or **ss**. Because this sound may be
spelled in several different ways, you must remember
each spelling.

|sh| a**sh**amed   emo**ti**on   so**ci**al   ti**ss**ue

Complete the Spelling Words on the apple slices
by writing the letters that spell the |sh| sound.
Then write each word in the pie with the
matching spelling pattern.

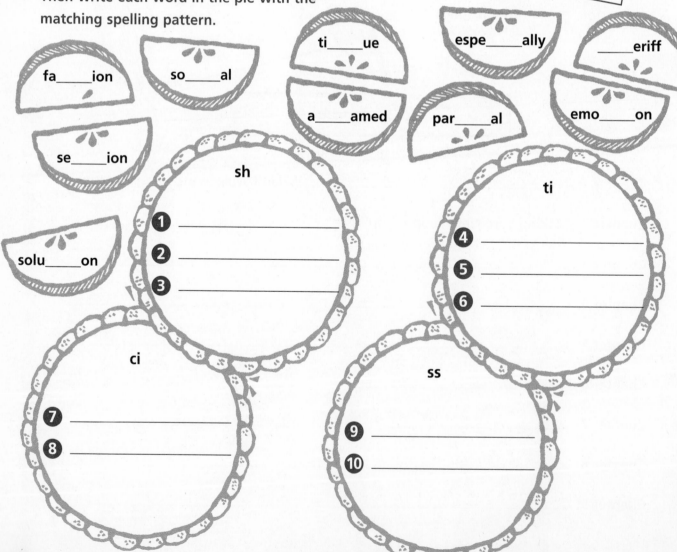

fa____ion

so____al

ti____ue

espe____ally

____eriff

se____ion

a____amed

par____al

emo____on

solu____on

sh

1 _____
2 _____
3 _____

ti

4 _____
5 _____
6 _____

ci

7 _____
8 _____

ss

9 _____
10 _____

Spelling Spree

Analogies
Decide which Spelling Word completes each analogy. Write the words on the auctioneer's hammer.

1. Teacher is to principal as deputy is to _____.
2. Apple is to fruit as fear is to _____.
3. Whole is to fractional as complete is to _____.
4. Metal is to gold as paper is to _____.
5. Money is to currency as style is to _____.
6. Campaign is to political as event is to _____.

Spelling Words

1. ashamed
2. social
3. especially
4. emotion
5. partial
6. solution
7. fashion
8. sheriff
9. tissue
10. session

1 _____
2 _____
3 _____
4 _____
5 _____
6 _____

Proofreading
Circle the four misspelled Spelling Words in this flier. Then write each word correctly.

Pie-Making Classes

Are you ashaimed of your hard, tasteless pie crusts? Do you find pie fillings expecially difficult to make? Do people avoid your pies at a social? If you have any of these problems, we have the solucion. Come to a seshun of our pie-making classes, held on Thursday nights.

For more information, call 555-4663.

7 _____
8 _____
9 _____
10 _____

Bidding Tips
Knowing how to bid at an auction is a special skill. What should a first-time auction bidder know? Write a list of tips for an inexperienced bidder. Use Spelling Words from the list.

....

Name

At the Social

Possessive Nouns Complete these notes for an article on the
pie social for the community newsletter. Write the correct possessive
form of the noun in parentheses.

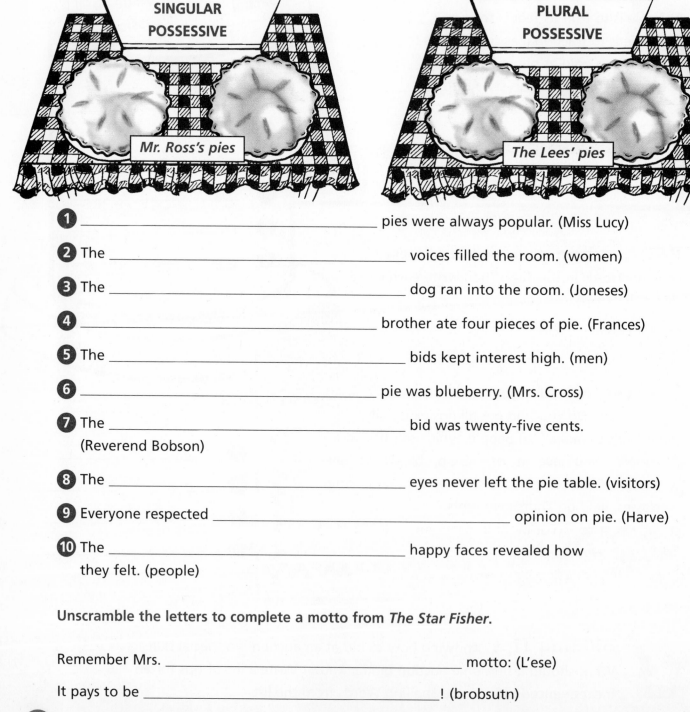

SINGULAR
POSSESSIVE

Mr. Ross's pies

PLURAL
POSSESSIVE

The Lees' pies

1 _____ pies were always popular. (Miss Lucy)

2 The _____ voices filled the room. (women)

3 The _____ dog ran into the room. (Joneses)

4 _____ brother ate four pieces of pie. (Frances)

5 The _____ bids kept interest high. (men)

6 _____ pie was blueberry. (Mrs. Cross)

7 The _____ bid was twenty-five cents.
(Reverend Bobson)

8 The _____ eyes never left the pie table. (visitors)

9 Everyone respected _____ opinion on pie. (Harve)

10 The _____ happy faces revealed how
they felt. (people)

Unscramble the letters to complete a motto from *The Star Fisher*.

Remember Mrs. _____ motto: (L'ese)

It pays to be _____! (brobsutn)

96 In Search of the Real Me

Name

Hink Pinks

Possessive Nouns There is going to be another social. This time some unusual items will be on display. Write labels for the items. Use each clue to write two rhyming words made up of a possessive noun and another noun that describes the item shown.

Example: desserts baked by Sy

Sy's pies

1 stories told by ocean mammals

2 large passenger vehicles belonging to Russ

3 pieces of pie belonging to small animals

4 sight organs of winged insects

5 paw coverings for a young cat

Extra! On a separate sheet of paper, make up some hink pinks of your own. Make sure your answers require the use of singular or plural possessive nouns. Illustrate your rhymes. Then give them to a classmate to solve.

Name

Some Good Advice

Read this letter to the school newspaper's advice columnist. Pick a character from this theme who would give good advice to this person. Write a response from that character. Answer the questions below to help you plan your letter.

Dear Problem Solver,

I'm having a hard time adjusting to my new school. Everyone here wears really expensive clothes, and I don't feel like I fit in at all. My parents say they can't afford to buy me the kind of outfits that will make me feel like I belong here. What do you think I should do?

Sincerely,
Fashionless in Florida

What similar experience has your character had?

_____

_____

What lesson did your character learn from that experience?

_____

_____

What conclusion would your character make about Fashionless in Florida's experience?

_____

_____

_____

Checklist

Check your letter with the list below.

☐ My letter gives advice to Fashionless in Florida.

☐ My letter gives advice I think my character would give.

☐ The advice in my letter tries to help Fashionless in Florida solve a problem.

Name

Unwrapping Ancient Mysteries

What mysteries will you unwrap? After reading each selection, complete the chart below and on the next page to show what facts you dug up and what you discovered.

	Into the Mummy's Tomb	Tales Mummies Tell
What treasures did the archaeologists uncover?		
What mysteries did the treasures reveal?		
What methods were used to solve the mysteries?		
What did the scientists discover?		
What details were most interesting to you?		

Unwrapping Ancient Mysteries

What mysteries will you unwrap? After reading each selection, complete the chart to show what facts you dug up and what you discovered.

	Dig This!	The Iceman
What treasures did the archaeologists uncover?		
What mysteries did the treasures reveal?		
What methods were used to solve the mysteries?		
What did the scientists discover?		
What details were most interesting to you?		

Name

A King's Burial: An Archaeologist's Find

Help bury an Egyptian king and then uncover the mystery.
First, cut out each item. Then, follow these directions.
As you do each step, say the boldfaced words aloud.

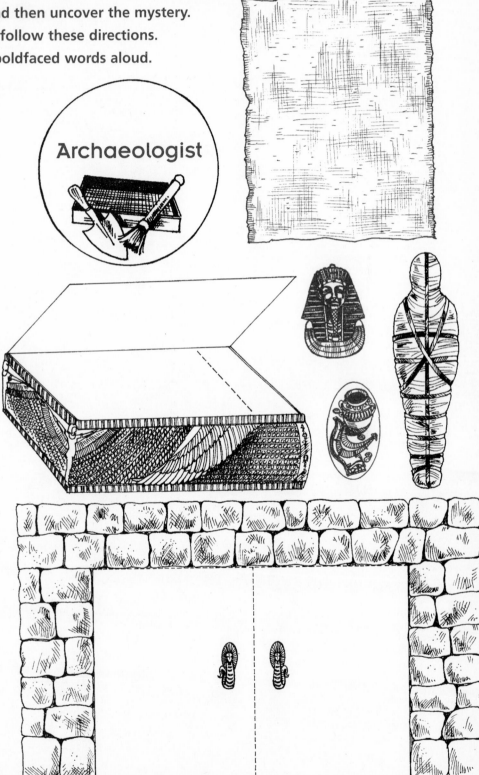

1 Wrap the **mummy** in the **shroud** and tape the shroud closed.

2 Tape the mask of the **pharaoh** onto the head of the **mummy.**

3 Cut a slit in the open **sarcophagus** along the dotted line. Slip the wrapped and masked **mummy** into the slit. Close the lid.

4 Cut along the dotted lines of the **tomb.** Open the doors. Place the **sarcophagus** inside.

5 Place the **artifacts** inside the **tomb** beside the **mummy.** Close the doors. Wait a few minutes. (Pretend you've waited three thousand years!)

6 Tape the **archaeologist** badge to your shirt. Open the **tomb,** take out the **artifacts,** open the lid of the **sarcophagus,** remove the **pharaoh's** mask, unwrap the **mummy** from its **shroud,** and call the reporters!

Name _____

Dateline: Missing Details!

This newspaper account of Howard Carter's discovery is almost complete. Fill in the missing details.

The London Journal

November 14, 1925

KING TUT FOUND!

The search for the burial site of King Tutankhamen is finally over. On November 4, 1922, a team of _____ led by _____ found the king's _____ hidden deep inside a cliff located in the Valley of the Kings. It took many months for the team to locate and reach the underground chamber where the _____, or ruler of ancient _____, had been buried.

Carter and his team discovered that the enormous, stone sarcophagus held three _____, each one more magnificent than the one before it. Inside the innermost one was the _____ wrapped in layers of linen bandages and decorated in _____.

The medical examination took place on November 11, 1925. After studying the fragile bones, the team determined that the king had been about _____ years old when he died. This fact, along with the careless construction of the shrine and the different faces on the masks, led the experts to wonder if the young pharaoh had been _____.

Name

Take a Closer Look!

Note three to six specific details about King Tut's coffin and mummy.

	Specific Details
Opening the Coffin What did the archaelogists find?	
Unwrapping the Mummy What did the doctors find?	

Name

Tut's Tomb Uncovered

**Imagine that you are a reporter in 1925. You have written this
newspaper account telling about Howard Carter's amazing
discovery. Your editor wants you to revise the article by
combining some of the shorter sentences.**

**In each paragraph, look for sentences that could be combined
into compound sentences. Rewrite the article on the lines.**

This week in Egypt, the tomb of King Tutankhamen was opened by an archaeological team led by Howard Carter. A spokesperson for the team announced that jewels covered the mummy of the king. The linens wrapping the mummy contained more than a hundred jewels. There were jeweled collars and pendants around the king's neck. On his fingers were thirteen rings.

Anatomy experts examined the bones this morning and made two new discoveries. The pharaoh was 5 feet, $5\frac{1}{8}$ inches tall. He was only about eighteen when he died. Doctors aren't certain about the cause of death. The pharaoh might have died in an accident. He may even have been murdered!

Carter told reporters he feels bad about disturbing the sacred tomb. He realizes that unwrapping the mummy will help the world learn more about ancient Egypt and its people.

_____

_____

_____

_____

_____

_____

_____

_____

_____

_____

_____

_____

Prefix Clues

Can you take apart words to find their meaning? Use these clues.

Prefix	Meaning	Prefix	Meaning
semi-	half, somewhat, or partly	*bi-*	two
uni-	one	*tri-*	three

Word Root	Meaning
pod, ped	foot or footlike part
lingua	tongue, language
later	side

1 The French flag is *tricolor*. What does that mean?

_____

2 A salon gives *unisex* haircuts. What kinds of haircuts are those?

_____

3 A recipe calls for *semisweet* chocolate chips. How will they taste?

_____

4 A *biplane* has how many sets of wings? How do you know?

_____

5 Kim was born in the United States. Her mother grew up in Japan.
Her father grew up in Germany. Kim is *trilingual*. What does that mean?

_____

6 Human beings are *bipedal* mammals. What does that mean?

_____

7 A photographer rested her camera on a kind of stand called a
tripod. Why does it have that name?

_____

8 A nation made a *unilateral* decision to control offshore fishing. Did that
nation sign an agreement with other nations? How do you know?

_____

Picture This An archaeologist discovered a sarcophagus on which
there was a drawing of some unusual creatures. Their skin was
semitransparent, their hair was bicolor, and their size was uniform. They
were also tripedal. Make a captioned drawing of two of these creatures.

Name

Steps Back in Time

Dr. I. M. Phinder is giving a speech but has left out some words.
Help him complete the speech. Some words will be from the selection:
archaeologist, artifacts, mummy, pharaoh, sarcophagus, shroud,
and **tomb.** The rest of the words are up to you.

I am so very glad you could join me tonight. As most of you know, I am an

_____ and have recently returned from Egypt, where it

hardly ever rains. The climate there is so very dry, in fact, that a good deal

of the land is desert. The hot sands serve as a natural preserver of sorts, so

we have been able to find many _____ still intact after

thousands of _____. This trip was very exciting because in

the cliffs above our camp in the desert we came upon a set of stairs that led

to an ancient _____, or burial chamber. There we found,

much to our surprise, a _____. We suspected that it might

belong to one _____ who ruled ancient Egypt during the

Middle Kingdom because the craftsmanship of the _____

covering the coffin was typical of that time. And indeed, on the linen

_____ covering the body of the long-dead king was a

painting of the pharaoh's face and _____ identifying the

ruler. Other hieroglyphs in the wall paintings lining the tomb told us the

story of this pharaoh's life. The wall paintings also depicted what this

_____ could expect to happen in the afterlife.

Name

Jeweled Endings

Adding *-ed* or *-ing* Each Spelling Word has *-ed* or *-ing* added to a base word. A **base word** is a word to which a beginning or an ending can be added. When a one-syllable base word ends with one vowel and one consonant, double the final consonant before adding *-ed* or *-ing.*

wrap + ed = wrapped   slip + ing = slipping

When a two-syllable base word ends with a stressed syllable, double the final consonant before adding *-ed* or *-ing.* Do not double the final consonant when the first syllable is stressed.

be<u>gin</u> + ing = beginning   <u>cov</u>er + ed = covered

Combine the base words and the endings to make Spelling Words. Write each Spelling Word in the sarcophagus.

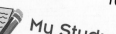

Spelling Words

1. wrapped
2. beginning
3. covered
4. happened
5. slipping
6. suffered
7. setting
8. entered
9. forgetting
10. preferred

My Study List
What other words do you need to study for spelling? Add them to My Study List for *Into the Mummy's Tomb* at the back of this book.

suffer + ed	forget + ing	set + ing
happen + ed	begin + ing	prefer + ed
wrap + ed	cover + ed	slip + ing
enter + ed		

Doubled Consonants

1 _____   4 _____

2 _____   5 _____

3 _____   6 _____

No Spelling Change

7 _____

8 _____

9 _____

10 _____

Spelling Spree

Proofreading Circle four misspelled Spelling Words in this log entry. Write each word correctly.

Thursday   An accident hapened today at the dig. I was on the roof of the tomb, begining my search for the entrance. Suddenly, the stones under me shifted, and I crashed down into the tomb. I am now coverred with scrapes and wrapped with bandages. I would have perferred not to be a living mummy, but at least I found the entrance!

Spelling Words

1. wrapped
2. beginning
3. covered
4. happened
5. slipping
6. suffered
7. setting
8. entered
9. forgetting
10. preferred

1 _____
2 _____
3 _____
4 _____

Mummy Memories Write the Spelling Word that best completes the mummy's thought.

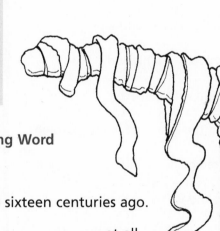

5 I _____ this tomb sixteen centuries ago.

6 I died suddenly, so I never _____ at all.

7 I remember people _____ my body on a table.

8 I remember how they _____ these bandages.

9 Look! One of my bandages is _____ off!

10 Oops! I keep _____ I'm a mummy!

Tunes from the Tomb Imagine that you are a mummy who used to be a songwriter. Write five song titles a mummy might write. Capitalize each important word in the titles. Use Spelling Words from the list.

Name

Window to the Past

TRANSITIVE

The explorer **spotted** the tomb.

INTRANSITIVE

The door **creaked** loudly.

Action Verbs and Direct Objects

Read each sentence. Draw an arrow from the action verb to any direct objects. Then write the verb on the door.

Example: King Tutankhamen ruled Egypt.

1. Tutankhamen died at a young age.

2. The Egyptians preserved his body.

3. They treated him with respect.

4. Thieves robbed the graves of many pharaohs.

5. Carter uncovered golden coffins and King Tut.

6. He traveled to the Valley of the Kings.

7. Callender and Carter spied the hidden steps.

8. They waved wildly to their team members.

9. The archaeologists published articles.

10. Their discovery serves as a window to the past.

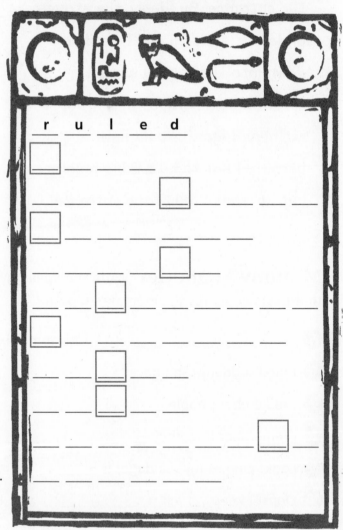

r u l e d

Write each boxed letter above the number of its sentence. You will answer the riddle *What do you call a serious archaeologist?*

A grave ___ ___ ___ ___ ___ ___ ___ ___ ___!
　　　　　 1　 2　 3　 4　 5　 6　 7　 8　 9

Name

Write On!

Action Verbs and Direct Objects Use each
word to create a sentence. Use the letters in the word to begin
each important word in the sentence. Use action verbs in all
sentences. At least two sentences should use intransitive
verbs. Underline any direct objects.

Example: (TOMB   **T**utankhamen **o**wned **m**any **b**racelets.

1 MASK _____

_____

_____

2 EGYPT _____

_____

_____

3 GOLD _____

_____

4 MUMMY _____

_____

5 NILE _____

_____

6 KING _____

_____

7 COFFIN _____

_____

8 THIEVES _____

_____

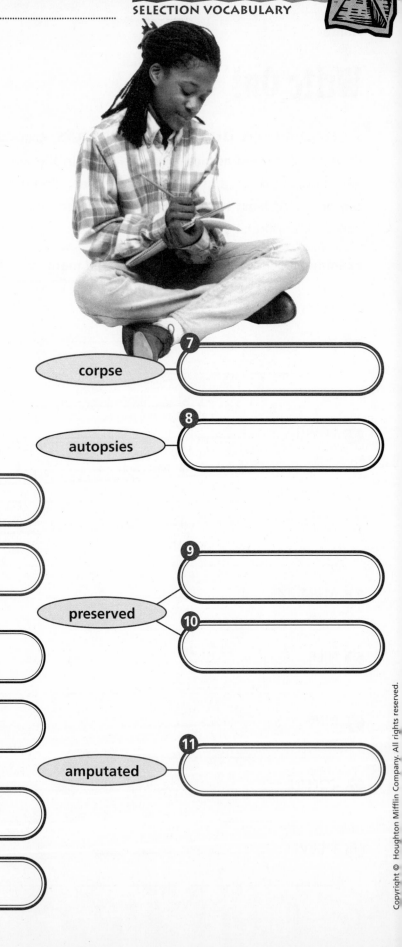

Word Webs

Use the words and phrases in the box to complete each word web.

- protected from decay
- cut off a limb
- set of clues
- mummy makers
- saved for the future
- body preparers
- studies of dead bodies
- dead body
- methods
- proof
- special ways of doing something

7 _____ corpse

8 _____ autopsies

1 _____
2 _____
evidence

9 _____
10 _____
preserved

3 _____
4 _____
embalmers

11 _____
amputated

5 _____
6 _____
techniques

112 Unwrapping Ancient Mysteries

Name _____

Mummy Tales

Label each statement T for True or F for False. If the statement is false, cross out words or add words to make it true.

1 _____ Scientists felt that Mummy 1770 was probably a male.

2 _____ The person lived about 300 years ago.

3 _____ One strange thing about Mummy 1770 is that the lower parts of both arms were missing.

4 _____ The rounded shape that showed up in x-rays close to the mummy's leg bones was a baby's head.

5 _____ In life, the person had been infected with Guinea worms.

6 _____ At one point, scientists suspected that the person had been attacked by an animal, perhaps a hippopotamus or a crocodile.

7 _____ Carbon-14 dating showed that Mummy 1770 had actually been wrapped four or five times.

8 _____ There was also evidence that Mummy 1770 had been damaged by water, repaired, and rewrapped.

9 _____ Because the wisdom teeth had not yet grown in, scientists estimated that the person was less than 20 years old at the time of death.

10 _____ Since the skull had broken into about 30 pieces, scientists were unable to make a clay model of what the person may have looked like.

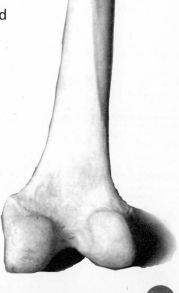

Name

Pay Close Attention

As you read the paragraph, think carefully about causes and effects. Then complete the organizer.

By the time Molly arrived at the museum, it had closed for the day. She was disappointed. The museum had advertised a new exhibit about the pyramids of Egypt. Ever since her class studied ancient Egypt, Molly was fascinated with mummies, pharaohs, tombs, and artifacts. Since she couldn't see the exhibit, she decided to go to the library. None of the newest books on ancient Egypt were in! Someone else must be as interested as she! On her way out, as Molly passed the video section, she noticed a title: *A Visit to the Pyramids*. "Well, it may not be an exhibit, but maybe it's the next best thing," Molly thought as she grabbed the video and headed to the checkout desk.

EFFECT

EFFECT

EFFECT

CAUSE
The museum was closed.

CAUSE

CAUSE

EFFECT
Molly was disappointed.

Step by Step

Use this page to plan your explanation.

Steps	Details

Name

Synonym Search!

Did you notice any synonyms in *Tales Mummies Tell*? They were there.
They're also in this puzzle. Each word comes from the selection; so does its
missing synonym. Fill in the blanks with the missing letters of the synonym.

1. reveal   __ x [ ] __ s __

2. study   __ x [ ] __ i __ n __

3. decayed   [ ] __ t __ t __ __

4. poorly   __ [ ] __ d __ __ y

5. puzzle   __ y [ ] __ t __ __ y

6. preserved   __ __ m __ m __ i __ [ ] __ d

7. broken   __ __ a __ c [ ] __ __ r __

8. body   __ __ r [ ]

Write the boxed letters to answer this question:
What object appeared in x-rays of Mummy 1770?

__ __ __ __ __ __ __ __

Sharpen Your Writing with Synonyms   It's very easy to
use the word *very* when a synonym would do a very good job. How
many synonyms can you list for the words shown?

very small	very fast
very big	**very slow**

Name

Mum's the Word!

Complete the crossword puzzle. Some of the words are from the selection vocabulary. The rest are words that you've read in *Tales Mummies Tell.* Good luck!

autopsies	amputated
corpse	embalmers
evidence	preserved
techniques	

Across

1. used to keep a damaged bone from moving
5. _____ Dundee!
7. proof
8. Jam is _____ fruit.
10. With _____ vision, you could see through many things.
12. wormlike form of insect
13. giant plant eaters found in rivers
14. procedures or methods
15. examinations that determine the cause of death

Down

1. surgeon's knife
2. the River _____
3. what you find in a tomb
4. Humans have 12 of these kinds of teeth.
6. what they didn't know about Mummy No. 1770
9. those who prepared mummies for the afterlife
11. severed a limb

Name ....

Final Endings

Adding Endings and Suffixes

Each Spelling Word was made by adding a suffix or
an ending to a base word that ends with **e**. A **suffix**
is a word part added to the end of a base word or a
word root.

When the suffix or ending begins with a vowel, the
final **e** is usually dropped from the base word. When
the suffix begins with a consonant, the final **e** is
usually kept.

BASE WORD	ENDING
prove + ed	= proved
like + ly	= likely
handle + ed	= handled

However, when the suffix **-ly** is added to a base
word that ends with the lll sound spelled with the
pattern **le,** the final **le** is dropped.

BASE WORD	ENDING
simple + ly	= simply

Combine the base word and ending.
Then write the Spelling Word.

Spelling Words

1. likely
2. proved
3. loosest
4. serving
5. closeness
6. simply
7. placement
8. shapeless
9. gently
10. handled

 My Study List
What other words do you
need to study for spelling?
Add them to My Study List
for *Tales Mummies Tell* in the back
of this book.

simple + ly	loose + est	handle + ed	close + ness
place + ment	like + ly	serve + ing	shape + less
	prove + ed	gentle + ly	

Final _e_ dropped	**Final _e_ kept**	**Final _le_ dropped**
1 _____	**5** _____	**9** _____
2 _____	**6** _____	**10** _____
3 _____	**7** _____	
4 _____	**8** _____	

Name _____

Spelling Spree

Write the Spelling Word that fits each clue.

Spelling Words

1. likely
2. proved
3. loosest
4. serving
5. closeness
6. simply
7. placement
8. shapeless
9. gently
10. handled

1 being of use; acting as

___ ___ ___ ___ ___ ___ ___
        2   7

2 nearness

___ ___ ___ ___ ___ ___ ___ ___ ___
 1   5

3 in a mild and soft manner

___ ___ ___ ___ ___ ___
        9

4 showed to be true

___ ___ ___ ___ ___ ___
          3   6

5 merely; just

___ ___ ___ ___ ___ ___
              8

6 arrangement

___ ___ ___ ___ ___ ___ ___ ___ ___
              4

Now write the numbered letters to complete this poem:

I might eat a body floating in the Nile,

Because I'm none other than a ___ ___ ___ ___ ___ ___ ___ ___ ___ !
                                 1   2   3   4   5   6   7   8   9

Proofreading Circle four
misspelled words in this list of rules.
Then write each word correctly.

7 _____

8 _____

9 _____

10 _____

- All mummies must be handeled with care.
- Never turn over a mummy; you are likly to damage it.
- Always cut the losest wrappings first.
- Remember, even the most shapeles mummies are treasures!

Mummy Wrap-Up Pretend you are an embalmer in ancient
Egypt. Write a set of wrapping directions for your helper. Use Spelling
Words from the list.

Which Is It?

Being and Linking Verbs Circle the verbs and underline the predicate nouns and predicate adjectives. Write each predicate noun or predicate adjective in the proper column in the chart.

1 The findings were a surprise to the scientists.

2 The mummy's teeth appeared surprisingly strong.

3 Dr. Rosalie David became the leader of the team.

4 The paint on the skull was a sign of an injury.

5 This girl seemed real to the researchers.

6 The feet on the mummy were artificial.

7 The mummy had been an unhealthy person.

8 The Manchester team felt pleased with the results.

9 The strange spot on the x-ray was a small worm.

10 The scientists' conclusions seemed very sensible.

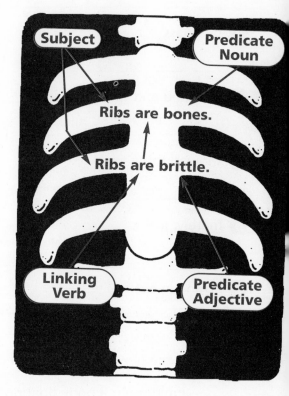

Predicate Nouns	Predicate Adjectives

....

Name

Solve the Mystery

Being and Linking Verbs   You have been asked to examine a skeleton
to identify it. Use the notes to complete your official report. Each sentence should
include a linking verb and a predicate noun or a predicate adjective. Use at least
four different linking verbs. Label each sentence **PN** or **PA** to show whether you
used a predicate noun or a predicate adjective.

Notes	
bones—thin	longer bones—hollow, light in weight
tail—fairly short	nose—beak
breastbone—quite large	body—suitable for flying
4 toes—long	neck—very flexible

Linking Verbs
is
are
seem/seems
appear/appears
feel/feels
look/looks

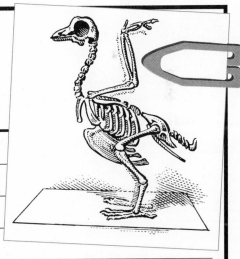

Report on Skeleton 1821

Date: _____

OBSERVATIONS

The bones _____

The longer bones _____

Also, they _____

Its neck _____

The nose of the creature _____

The four toes _____

Its breastbone _____

The tail _____

Its body _____

Identification: What kind of animal is it? __It is_____

Name

Digging for Synonyms

Sift through the words and phrases and organize them in the
synonym chart. Throw away three words but preserve all the rest.

	rotted		societies		slippery	
	peel		ancient		banana	what's left
	location		lifestyles		decayed	before written record
	remainder from the past			place where something was		

	SYNONYM	SYNONYM
cultures		
prehistoric		
decomposed		
site		
ruins		

Dig This Interview!

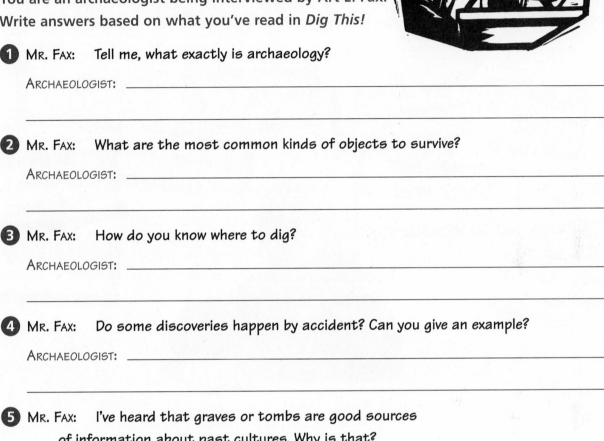

You are an archaeologist being interviewed by Art E. Fax.
Write answers based on what you've read in *Dig This!*

1 MR. FAX: Tell me, what exactly is archaeology?

ARCHAEOLOGIST: _____

_____

2 MR. FAX: What are the most common kinds of objects to survive?

ARCHAEOLOGIST: _____

_____

3 MR. FAX: How do you know where to dig?

ARCHAEOLOGIST: _____

_____

4 MR. FAX: Do some discoveries happen by accident? Can you give an example?

ARCHAEOLOGIST: _____

_____

5 MR. FAX: I've heard that graves or tombs are good sources
of information about past cultures. Why is that?

ARCHAEOLOGIST: _____

_____

6 MR. FAX: People talk about "excavation units." What are they?

ARCHAEOLOGIST: _____

_____

7 MR. FAX: What happens to the objects you dig up?

ARCHAEOLOGIST: _____

_____

8 MR. FAX: What is the hardest part of your job?

ARCHAEOLOGIST: _____

_____

....

Name

Support This!

Your team of archaeologists has finished a major dig. You're surrounded by notecards on specific details. Organize them under the main ideas.

beautiful silver mask

scrap of water-damaged cloth

perfect gold earring

potsherd

aerial photograph

undamaged iron cooking pot

report from an oil driller

waterlogged, broken piece of carved wood

computer printout of local plant life

x-ray of a bone

Main Ideas

• **Many artifacts are damaged or broken.** _____

_____

_____

_____

• **Many other artifacts are in excellent shape.** _____

_____

_____

_____

• **Technology helped make this dig successful.** _____

_____

_____

_____

Name

In Your Own Words

Paraphrase the information in each paragraph below.

Archaeological studies not only tell us about the past but also can help us solve problems in the present and in the future. Studying bones and skeletons can give scientists valuable information about disease. Old bones may provide the key to finding out whether certain diseases are caused by diet, living conditions, heredity, or climate. Rediscovered plants might feed future populations or be used in medicines.

_____

_____

_____

_____

_____

_____

Among New Mexico's many impressive archaeological sites is Pueblo Bonito, which is located in Chaco Canyon about one hundred miles south of Mesa Verde. Built by prehistoric Anasazi Indians, it resembles an ancient apartment house. The structure includes eight hundred rooms and outer walls built four stories high. The walls have no doors—the inhabitants climbed through small openings and used ladders to enter or exit their homes.

_____

_____

_____

_____

_____

Name

Hidden Words

Find and circle words with a suffix meaning "someone who" or "something that." The words go from top to bottom and from left to right. Then write each word in the box that contains its suffix.

CLUES

1. Something that toasts bread
2. Someone who begs
3. Someone who operates a train engine
4. Someone who takes photographs
5. Something that repels insects
6. Someone who gardens
7. Someone who works at a library
8. Someone who runs for political office
9. Someone who serves on a jury
10. Someone who plays the piano
11. Someone who climbs mountains
12. Someone who directs a movie

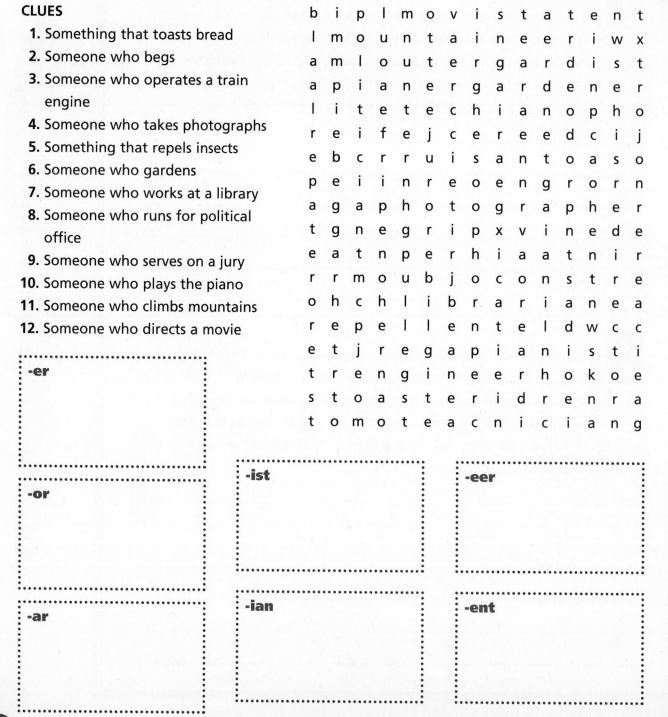

```
b i p l m o v i s t a t e n t
l m o u n t a i n e e r i w x
a m l o u t e r g a r d i s t
a p i a n e r g a r d e n e r
l i t e t e c h i a n o p h o
r e i f e j c e r e e d c i j
e b c r r u i s a n t o a s o
p e i i n r e o e n g r o r n
a g a p h o t o g r a p h e r
t g n e g r i p x v i n e d e
e a t n p e r h i a a t n i r
r r m o u b j o c o n s t r e
o h c h l i b r a r i a n e a
r e p e l l e n t e l d w c c
e t j r e g a p i a n i s t i
t r e n g i n e e r h o k o e
s t o a s t e r i d r e n r a
t o m o t e a c n i c i a n g
```

-er

-or

-ar

-ist

-ian

-eer

-ent

Name _____

Future Finds

In the year 5067, a team of archaeologists from Jupiter is sent to Earth
on a special mission. Unfortunately, static from a meteor shower has
interfered with transmission of their message home. Decipher it by filling
in the vocabulary words.

prehistoric	site	ruins	cultures	decomposed

Electronic Bulletin to Jupiter Satellite from Earth Excavation, Mission 261,

Northwest Quadrant, Solar Date 4.23.5067:   We have discovered a valuable

_____ that may have once been the location of a major urban

population center. Since the Atlantic Ocean has risen substantially over the past

ten centuries due to the melting of the polar ice caps, the area is under water.

Before launching the submarines, we used sonar to detect the

_____ of this toppled city. We had anticipated that many

things would have _____ or disintegrated by now. Luckily, the

sea water has served as a preserver of sorts. We are surprised to find so many

artifacts still intact: We have discovered one entire city block of skyscrapers that

we would like to bring back for display. We believe such habitats of Earth

_____ would make an excellent exhibit at the Intergalactic

Museum. Although some researchers regard the technology of this era as nearly

_____ compared to our own highly advanced society, we have

found evidence of a worldwide computerized communications system.

Sift and Sort

Adding -ion and -ation Each pair of Spelling Words includes a verb and a noun. The noun is formed by adding the suffix **-ion** or **-ation** to the verb.

VERBS: construct   inform

NOUNS: construction   information

If the verb ends with **e,** drop the **e** before adding **-ion** or **-ation.**

VERBS: locate   explore

NOUNS: location   exploration

Spelling Words

1. locate
2. location
3. inform
4. information
5. construct
6. construction
7. explore
8. exploration
9. examine
10. examination

My Study List

What other words do you need to study for spelling? Add them to My Study List for *Dig This!* in the back of this book.

Help the archaeologist sift the words. In the sifting screen, write the word pairs in which the e is dropped when *-ion* or *-ation* is added to the verb. Below the screen, write the word pairs in which there is no spelling change.

1. _____
2. _____
3. _____
4. _____
5. _____
6. _____

7. _____
8. _____
9. _____
10. _____

Name

Spelling Spree

Proofreading Circle five misspelled Spelling
Words in the telegram. Then write each word correctly.

Spelling Words

1. locate
2. location
3. inform
4. information
5. construct
6. construction
7. explore
8. exploration
9. examine
10. examination

TELEGRAM

HURRAH. STOP. FOUND LOCASION OF ANCIENT TEMPLE.
STOP. YOUR INFOMATION WAS HELPFUL. STOP. WILL
EXPLORE SITE CAREFULLY. STOP. EXPECT YOU WILL
WANT TO EXAMENE ALL FINDS. STOP. OUR
EXPLOREATION WILL HOLD UP CONSTRUCTION OF NEW
BUILDING. STOP. PLEASE ENFORM CREW OF DELAY.

1 _____

2 _____

3 _____

4 _____

5 _____

Label Your Finds Write the Spelling Word that is a
synonym or an antonym of each clue. Then write **S** if the
word is a synonym. Write **A** if the word is an antonym.

	Clues	Spelling Word	Synonym or Antonym
6	build		
7	inspection		
8	lose		
9	search		
10	demolition		

Digging for News You are about to interview a famous archaeologist.
Write your interview questions. Use Spelling Words from the list.

On Schedule

Singular Subject	Plural Subject
 The student <u>works</u> carefully.	 The students <u>work</u> carefully.

Subject-Verb Agreement Complete the schedule. First, show whether the subject of each sentence is singular or plural by putting a check mark in the correct box. Then write the verbs correctly.

	EXCAVATION SCHEDULE	✔ Singular	✔ Plural
June	**1.** A pilot _____ (fly) over the site.		
	2. A photographer _____ (snap) pictures		
July	**3.** A team member _____ (discuss) the dig with the landowner.		
	4. She _____ (resolve) any problem.		
Aug.	**5.** The archaeologists _____ (visit) the site.		
	6. They _____ (prepare) the final plans.		
	7. We _____ (be) available for any assignment.		
Sept.	**8.** The surveyor _____ (map) the site.		
	9. An excavator and an assistant _____ (mark) the grids.		
	10. You _____ (support) their work.		
Oct.	**11.** Diggers _____ (arrive) at the site.		
	12. I _____ (be) at the site daily.		
Nov.	**13.** _____ (Be) you in the lab this month?		
	14. Volunteers _____ (record) notes on objects.		
	15. An expert _____ (study) the artifacts.		

Name

Extra! Extra!

Subject-Verb Agreement Complete each headline by writing a verb in the present tense. Use the verbs in the box or ones of your own.

locate	try
fascinate	leave
discover	work
lend	be

1 **The Epitaph**

GUESTS _____

MUMMY IN KOFF INN

2 THE ARTIFACT

Trash _____

students of archaeology

3 **The Jurassic Journal**

VOLUME 1

JANUARY

Unknown person _____ a hand to museum

4 THE MUMMY MONITOR

Robbed archaeologist

_____ to get his

mummy back

5 **THE DAILY DIGGER**

Diggers _____

skeleton in closet

6 **The Excavator**

Failed expeditions _____

archaeologist's career in ruins

7 The Midnight Crier

"Destruction of the tomb _____

a tragedy," Dr. Wong says gravely

8 THE ANCIENT ENQUIRER

Skeleton crew _____ in

cemetery after storm

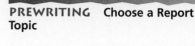

Name

I Wish I Knew All About...

Topic Ideas

▲ cave paintings of Lascaux

▲ ancient kingdom of Benin

▲ Komodo dragon

▲ making dollar bills

▲ Klondike gold rush

▲ the real Robinson Crusoe

▲ Easter Island

▲ Hopi Kachinas

▲ Amelia Earhart

▲ Nobel Peace Prize

▲ King Kamehameha the Great

▲ the job of a police detective

My Ideas for a Research Report
Write five topics that you would like to research.

_____

_____

_____

_____

_____

Is this topic too big for a two- or three-page report? How can I narrow it?

Does this topic really interest me?

Think about each idea you listed. Ask yourself these questions about each one. You may want to discuss your ideas with a classmate. Then write the topic you want to research.

_____

_____

_____

Would I be able to find information about this topic easily?

What Do You Want to Know?

What do you want to find out about your topic? Write your topic on the
file box. Then write five questions you want to answer about your topic.
Write one question on each file card.

Sources   What sources will you use? What people can you interview for information?

_____

_____

_____

_____

Name

Another Look

Reread and revise your report. Put a check mark next to each question after you have revised your report for that question.

• Revising Checklist •

☐ Does the introduction present the topic and lead into the report?

☐ Did I write topic sentences that state main ideas?

☐ Did I give supporting details?

☐ Does each paragraph lead logically to the next?

☐ Does the conclusion sum up the main ideas?

Questions for a Writing Conference

• Which part is most interesting?

• Which parts are not clear?

• Does any information seem out of order?

• Where are more facts needed?

• Could the introduction or closing be improved? How?

Write notes to help you remember the comments and ideas mentioned in your writing conference.

_____

_____

_____

_____

_____

_____

Name

Words That Chill

Organize these words and phrases into the antonym chart. Remember that an antonym is a word or words opposite in meaning. Dig out two antonyms for each vocabulary word. If you're stuck on a word that doesn't fit as an antonym—leave it frozen!

melted ice shelter modern protection civilized state precisely know exactly professionals puddles arrows bows experts

	ANTONYM	ANTONYM
amateurs		
primitive		
estimate		
exposure		
glaciers		

Name

Iceman FactFind

For each multiple-choice question, circle the best answer.

1 Who discovered the Iceman's frozen body?
a. two mountain hikers
b. Dr. Rainer Henn
c. a prehistoric hunter
d. a group of boys playing in the hills

2 What did scientists find beside the mummy?
a. a huge bow and an ax
b. a pair of slippers
c. the skeleton of a dog
d. a strange metal box

3 What did Dr. Spindler guess?
a. Ötzi was a wealthy king.
b. Ötzi was the oldest mummy ever found.
c. Ötzi was only 400 years old.
d. Ötzi was too damaged to study.

4 In which time did the Iceman live?
a. the 1800s
b. the third century
c. the Copper Age: 5000 years ago
d. the age of the dinosaurs

5 What did people do in the time in which the Iceman lived?
a. built wood and mud houses
b. used plows for farming
c. raised animals
d. all of the above

6 Which fact is true of the Iceman's appearance?
a. He was over 6 feet tall.
b. He had straight blonde hair.
c. He was thin and weak.
d. He had tattoos.

7 How did the Iceman die?
a. a knife wound
b. a blow to the head
c. exposure to the cold
d. poison

8 What did the Iceman wear?
a. leather pants and jacket
b. shoes stuffed with hay
c. a huge grass cape
d. all of the above

9 What was inside the Iceman's leather pouch?
a. a letter
b. a jar of seeds
c. two pieces of flint
d. a valuable jewel

10 Which is true of the Iceman's arrows?
a. carried in a deerskin quiver
b. lost in his accident
c. broken into many pieces
d. made by machines

Facts and Opinions

**Three statements are facts. Three are opinions. Beside each write FACT
or OPINION to show that you understand the difference.**

1 _____ The Iceman was the greatest archaeological find ever.

2 _____ Ötzi's wooden bow was six feet long.

3 _____ Ötzi's ax blade was made of copper.

4 _____ Ötzi was probably a shepherd or a medicine man.

5 _____ Two hikers found the frozen corpse in the mountains.

6 _____ Ötzi's friends may have searched for him.

**For each of the opinions below, check whether you agree or disagree.
Then choose one statement and give the reasons for your opinion.
Use facts from the selection to support your opinion.**

		AGREE	DISAGREE
7	Ötzi was a very strong man.	☐	☐
8	Ötzi was well loved by his family.	☐	☐
9	Ötzi died a terrible and tragic death.	☐	☐
10	Ötzi is a great teacher.	☐	☐

_____

_____

_____

_____

_____

_____

Name _____

Help Wanted

Imagine you are editing your draft of a newspaper story. First, write the correct tense of each verb that is in parentheses. Then add two lines to the story by writing a new sentence. Use an insert mark (∧) to show where in the story you want to insert the sentence.

Hikers _____ (Discover) **5500 Year-Old Mummy**

by I. Canwright Well

Yesterday, two hikers, Erika and Helmut Simon, _____ (find)

the remains of a human body on a mountain trail near the Italian

border. When they _____ (notice) a small hole in

the skull, they _____ (suspect) murder. Immediately,

they _____ (contact) the Italian police. Now, as other

hikers _____ (visit) the scene and

_____ (take) items from the body,   *Which tenses*
should
people _____ (speculate) about the   *I use?*

identity of the mysterious person. Soon, the Austrian police

_____ (remove) the body from the thick ice. They

_____ (study) it carefully and slowly. Hopefully, they

_____ (determine) his identity soon.

_____

_____

_____

_____

138 Unwrapping Ancient Mysteries

What's the Category?

Read the words listed together. Then write the name of each category in the box below the arrow. Add one more word to each list.

1 BOAR   IBEX
ANTELOPE   DEER
_____

2 BARLEY
PEAS   FLAX
_____

3 VIBURNUM   ASH
YEW   BIRCH
_____

Here are more words arranged in categories. Circle the one boldface word that belongs in the category. Then explain why you chose that word.

4 archaeologist, scientist, historian   **amateur**   **researcher**

_____

_____

5 copper, bronze, wood   **plastic**   **metal**

_____

_____

6 coffin, mummy, corpse   **ancestor**   **tomb**

_____

_____

7 knife, arrowhead, bow   **weapon**   **slingshot**

_____

_____

8 mountain, valley, glacier   **storm**   **lake**

_____

_____

Name

Word Webs

Choose words or phrases from the box to complete the word webs.

without protection	long ago
for love, not money	little skill
in plain sight	judgment
slowly moving	approximate
early history	icy

primitive

exposure

glaciers

estimate

amateurs

Stilt Sort

More Words with *-ion* Each pair of Spelling Words includes a verb and a noun. The noun is formed by adding the suffix *-ion* to the verb. In each verb, the final ***d*** changes to another consonant when *-ion* is added. Knowing how the spelling changes in one pair of words may help you predict changes in words with similar spelling patterns.

VERBS: decide   intend

NOUNS: decision   intention

Spelling Words

1. decide
2. decision
3. conclude
4. conclusion
5. attend
6. attention
7. erode
8. erosion
9. intend
10. intention

My Study List
What other words do you need to study for spelling? Add them to My Study List for *The Iceman* at the back of this book.

Write each pair of Spelling Words on the correct stilt house.

d changes to *s*

d changes to *t*

1 _____

2 _____

3 _____

4 _____

5 _____

6 _____

7 _____

8 _____

9 _____

10 _____

Spelling Spree

Spelling Words

1. decide
2. decision
3. conclude
4. conclusion
5. attend
6. attention
7. erode
8. erosion
9. intend
10. intention

Proofreading   Circle four misspelled Spelling Words in this news release. Write each word correctly.

Officials intend to reach a deciseon soon on the fate of Ötzi, the Iceman. Atention is being paid to concerns of both Italy and Austria. Officials may cunclude that the two countries should share the mummy. No one wants relations between the countries to eroad over this issue.

1 _____

2 _____

3 _____

4 _____

Archaeologists at Work   Write a Spelling Word for each underlined clue in this conversation between two archaeologists.

5   "Now that we're near the end of our study, have you figured out how the mummy's face was damaged?"

6   "I can't make up my mind yet."

8   "It's difficult to know what role the process of being worn away played in the damage."

7   "Well, do you plan to make a guess?"

9   "Perhaps we should be present at next week's talk on that topic."

10   "It is my aim to go. After all, I am the speaker."

5 _____   6 _____

7 _____   8 _____

9 _____   10 _____

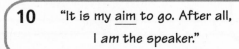 **Ötzi's Last Words**   Suppose Ötzi had had a chance to write a few last words to his family and friends. Write his farewell note. Use Spelling Words from the list.

Window into History

The Iceman <u>carried</u> a pack.

The hiker <u>carries</u> a pack.

Future explorers will carry packs.

Verb Tenses Complete the poem by writing the verb in the tense given.

The Iceman

A man _____ for his life .... (*struggle*, past)
In a storm long ago.

Sadly, he _____ alone .... (*die*, past)
In the ice and the snow.

How old _____ the Iceman? .... (*be*, present)

His ax _____ the clue. .... (*provide*, past)

His other possessions _____ .... (*be*, past)
Important clues too.

They _____ a life .... (*reveal*, past)
Rather peaceful, not alarming.

Of people who _____ .... (*live*, past)
By hunting, fishing, and farming.

With Ötzi's preserved mummy,

A scientist _____ his looks. .... (*study*, past)

Artists _____ ancient people. .... (*imagine*, present)

They _____ their pictures for books. .... (*draw*, present)

I _____ through a small window .... (*look*, present)
Into past history.

The past _____ .... (*remain*, future)
A big mystery to me.

Unwrapping Ancient Mysteries 143

Name _____

Imagine That!

Verb Tenses Imagine that you have been frozen in ice and are revived 5000 years from today. A reporter wants to interview you about your memories of life in the twentieth century and your thoughts about life fifty centuries from now. Write answers to the reporter's questions. Use verbs in the present, past, and future tenses.

1 What did your home look like?

_____

_____

_____

2 What did your clothes look like?

_____

_____

_____

3 What do you like best about our life in the seventieth century?

_____

_____

_____

4 What do you like least?

_____

_____

_____

5 What will you do first tomorrow?

_____

_____

_____

Name

Analyzing an Artifact

Choose an object of the present time and analyze it as an archaeologist might do. You may want to reread parts of *Unwrapping Ancient Mysteries* to help you plan your presentation.

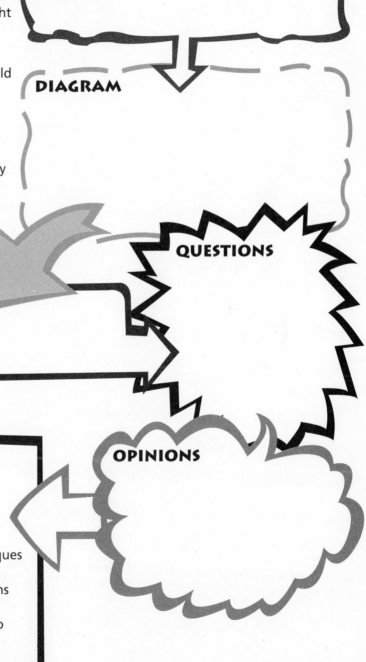

1. **Choose an interesting artifact.** A regular shoe would be okay, but a soccer cleat might be more interesting.

2. **Draw a diagram of your artifact as it will be found.** What surroundings would help explain your artifact? How might it change over time? Would it fade, rust, or rot? Show details in your diagram.

3. **Play the role of the archaeologist.** Imagine you've never seen the object. Study it and note details. Ask yourself questions such as "What is the hardened material on the bottom?" Give opinions such as "The hardened material is probably mud." Last, note procedures to test your opinions.

ARTIFACT

DIAGRAM

QUESTIONS

DETAILS

OPINIONS

✔ **LIST**

My presentation—
❑ includes examples of archaeological techniques
❑ includes details, questions, and opinions about my artifact
❑ suggests procedures to test my opinions

Name

Imagination at Work

How does the imagination work? After reading each selection, fill in the chart below and on the next page to show what journeys and discoveries you can find in the imagination at work.

	The Phantom Tollbooth	Faith Ringgold
How was the imagination at work here?		
What inspires the mind to be creative?		
What sort of discovery or journey did the imagination bring about?		
What is the connection between creativity and invention?		

Name

Imagination at Work

How does the imagination work? After reading each selection, fill
in the chart to show what journeys and discoveries you can find in
the imagination at work.

	The Moon and I	The Wright Brothers
How was the imagination at work here?		
What inspires the mind to be creative?		
What sort of discovery or journey did the imagination bring about?		
What is the connection between creativity and invention?		

Name

Token Talk

Use the word tokens to take you to Fantasyville. Draw a line from each token to the slot below the question it answers.

1 In what way would you be walking if you were going slowly, dragging your feet, head down, a sad expression on your face?

2 In what way might you speak if you told someone about the new red bike you wished you could have?

3 What are you doing when you put off saving money for the bike until next month?

4 What do you have when you plan a trip on your new bike?

Name

A Letter to the Editor

Suppose Milo wrote a letter to the editor about his journey.
Fill in the spaces to help get his message across.

To the Editor:

Perhaps your readers think that life is boring. Well, let me tell you something that happened to me the other day. I was hanging out in my room because nothing really _____ _____ me. And I saw this huge package with a note on it that said _____ _____. In it was a _____, which I quicky assembled.

Also included were four other things: _____ _____. I got into my electric car and headed for_____. I thought it was only a _____, but when I found myself on an actual _____, I knew this was _____. Suddenly, I was in _____, where I met _____. Then the bright countryside turned gray and I was in _____ _____. And guess how I got out: by_____!

Lights, Camera, Fantasy

You're the acting coach on the set of *The Phantom Tollbooth, The Movie*. Help the actors playing the parts of Milo and the watchdog understand their roles. Identify traits and events. List them in two columns: Real and Fantastic.

Milo

REAL   FANTASTIC

_____   _____
_____   _____
_____   _____
_____   _____

The watchdog

REAL   FANTASTIC

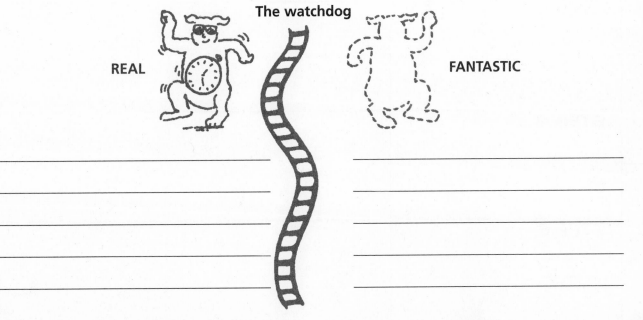

_____   _____
_____   _____
_____   _____
_____   _____

 Imagination at Work 151

Name

Writing Instructions

Use this page to plan instructions for something you know how to do well. Write each step of your instructions, and list details that your audience would need to know to do each one.

MATERIALS

STEPS	DETAILS
STEP 1	
STEP 2	
STEP 3	
STEP 4	
STEP 5	

Name

Get Lost!

Write the word that answers each clue. Then circle the word's homophone in the story about the boy and his father.

write	mane
rode	weak
threw	hour
new	lead
won	maid

T O L L B O O T H

Last week, my dad and I got lost. We were on a main highway, so Dad asked the man in a tollbooth for directions. The man said he knew the way. He said to turn right at the stop sign, go straight for one mile, and go through two sets of lights. We made our way along and figured all was well until we saw where the road had led us—back to the tollbooth!

1 a horse's neck hair

_____

2 not strong

_____

3 sixty minutes

_____

4 the opposite of **old**

_____

5 material inside a pencil

_____

10 a woman housekeeper

_____

9 went on horseback

_____

8 came in first place

_____

7 flung

_____

6 put ideas on paper

_____

 Imagination at Work   153

Name

The Phantom Coin Box

You're a feature writer for the *Fantasy Times*. You've just interviewed Milo's teenage cousin, Pat, who's been dissatisfied with her life until receiving a phantom coin box. Using the words in the box, draft the lead paragraph of an article about Pat's adventures.

expectations	wistfully	strenuous
speculate	dawdle	procrastinating
accomplished	dejectedly	

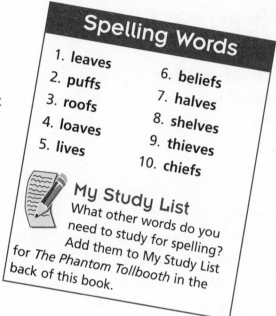

Name

Get Out of the Doldrums

Plurals of Words Ending with *f*

Each Spelling Word is the plural form of a noun that ends with *f*, *ff*, or *fe*. Remember these guidelines to form the plurals.

- Words ending with *f*: add *-s* or change the *f* to *v* and add *-es*.

- Words ending with *ff*: add *-s*.

- Words ending with *fe*: change the *f* to *v* and add *-s*.

roof	leaf	puff	life
roofs	leaves	puffs	lives

Spelling Words

1. leaves
2. puffs
3. roofs
4. loaves
5. lives
6. beliefs
7. halves
8. shelves
9. thieves
10. chiefs

My Study List

What other words do you need to study for spelling? Add them to My Study List for *The Phantom Tollbooth* in the back of this book.

Help Milo get out of the Doldrums. Write the Spelling Word that is the plural form of the noun on each Lethargarian.

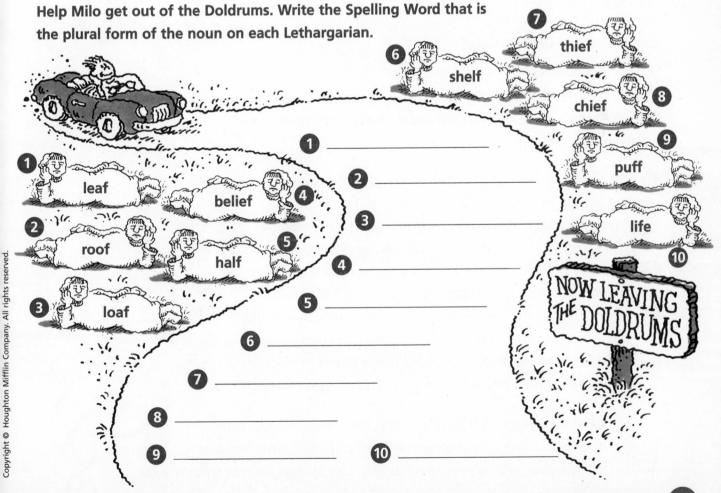

1 _____

2 _____

3 _____

4 _____

5 _____

6 _____

7 _____

8 _____

9 _____

10 _____

Spelling Spree

Proofreading Milo might have found this town more interesting than the Doldrums. Find and circle five misspelled Spelling Words in the paragraph. Then write each word correctly.

Spelling Words

1. leaves
2. puffs
3. roofs
4. loaves
5. lives
6. beliefs
7. halves
8. shelves
9. thieves
10. chiefs

Our town is also unique even though our belieffs and customs differ from those of the Lethargarians. In autumn, for example, the leeves fall up instead of down. Our loavs of bread are heart-shaped rather than round or rectangular. Our thieves give you things instead of taking things away. The fire chieves use milk instead of water to put out fires. Finally, instead of polluting the air, the pufs of smoke from our factories make the air cleaner.

1 _____

2 _____

3 _____

4 _____

5 _____

Whether Man Words Finish each quotation from the Whether Man with the Spelling Word that fits best. Write your words on the Whether Man's balloons.

6 "My, my, my, my, my, just look at the sun, the sun, the sun, shining on the ____ of those houses."

7 "Well now, well now, I don't know if you have to know what I know about how wholes become ____."

8 "Here in Expectations we expect— oh, yes, we expect—to spend our entire ____ expecting."

9 "Why no, why no, robbers and ____ are unwelcome, indeed not welcome, here in our land, the land of Expectations."

10 "You see, you see, those ____ hold many books of rules, rules and regulations, about what always or never to do."

6 _____

7 _____

8 _____

9 _____

10 _____

 Outrageous Ordinances The Doldrums had some outrageous laws. On a separate sheet of paper, write imaginary ordinances you would enact in your town or city. Use Spelling Words from the list.

Name _____

Verb Ticktacktoe

	Verb	Present Participle	Past	Past Participle
Regular	arrive	(is) arriving	arrived	(has) arrived
Irregular	lose	(is) losing	lost	(has) lost

Regular and Irregular Verbs As Milo talks to the Lethargarians, he keeps leaving out words. Help him by filling in the past, past participle, or present participle form of each verb.

Example: I am <u>wondering</u> what to do.
          wonder

First I _____ to find Dictionopolis but I _____
                    1 want   2 find

Expectations instead. I finally _____ a road sign for Dictionopolis, but
                                          3 see

now I have _____ my way again. Won't you stay awake and help me?
                    4 lose

You are _____ all the time. In fact, you have _____
                    5 yawn   6 do

nothing but nap since I _____. If you are _____
                                 7 arrive   8 look

for me later, don't be surprised if I have_____!
                                                    9 leave

Now play ticktacktoe. Write I or R to tell whether each verb you wrote with the matching number is regular or irregular.

①	②	③
④	⑤	⑥
⑦	⑧	⑨

Name _____

Tour Your Imagination!

Regular and Irregular Verbs You are
Milo's guide on a tour through Zestopolis. Use
different principal parts of the verbs provided or
your own verbs to write what you would tell him
about each sight.

bounce	drive	lose	stand
bring	feel	ring	swim
bubble	find	fly	take
dance	go	see	tell

1 Dynamall _____

_____

2 Dancing Rocks _____

_____

3 Animated Forest _____

_____

4 Lake Bubbly _____

_____

Name

A Few Words About Art

Use the vocabulary words to complete this museum plaque describing *Church Picnic,* one of Faith Ringgold's story quilts.

heritage	abstract	convey	composition
medium	legacy	dimension	

Church Picnic is a bright and colorful

_____ showing us the upbeat

mood of southern African Americans at the turn of the

century. Over thirty-six square feet in area, ***Church***

Picnic celebrates Faith Ringgold's roots and African

American cultural _____. Unlike

her earlier _____ canvases,

Church Picnic represents over 35 realistic figures.

Ringgold uses the _____ of paint

on canvas and quilting to produce this quilted

painting. In the quilted patchwork border, she has

written a sad love story to add a tragic

_____ to the scene. This story also

helps to _____ the importance of

storytelling in Ringgold's heritage. All in all, ***Church***

Picnic is one more part of the rich

_____ that Faith Ringgold has

given to us all.

Name

The Artful Truth

Read each sentence. Write a T if it is true and an F if it is false. If a sentence is false, write the correct sentence.

1 _____ Faith Ringgold always knew she would make quilts.

_____

2 _____ Ringgold named her painting *Dah #3* because it's what her grandchild called it.

_____

3 _____ Ringgold calls some of her pieces "story quilts" because people use them to snuggle under when reading stories to children.

_____

4 _____ *Church Picnic* is a story quilt that celebrates Faith Ringgold's Irish American heritage.

_____

5 _____ Cee Cee Prince is an example of a fictional character Ringgold created for her art.

_____

6 _____ Ringgold has never traveled outside the United States.

_____

7 _____ Ringgold performed a play in the 1980s that told about the way she lost 100 pounds.

_____

8 _____ The French Collection is Ringgold's collection of famous paintings by French artists.

_____

9 _____ Sometimes Ringgold uses her own family members in her art.

_____

10 _____ Today Ringgold divides her time between teaching and making art.

_____

Piecing the Details Together

What does the George Washington Bridge represent in
Faith Ringgold's artwork? Note details on the quilt on
page 375 and look for details in the selection. Write the
details that answer each question.

What are the women on the bridge doing?
How many women are on the bridge?
What do the women have in common?
How does the bridge look like a quilt?
What does the border of the quilt look like?
On page 382, what do you learn about the location of Ringgold's new studio?

Life Line

Once you have chosen the person you want to write about, you will need to do some research at the library. Use this time line to record and organize biographical events.

- Use the time line to write down your notes.
- Be sure to arrange the events in chronological order.

The Life of _____

DATE	EVENT

Name

Quilting Bee

Below is one completed quilt and one that hasn't been put together yet. Cut out the pieces of the incomplete quilt and assemble it. Make sure that each definition in your new quilt is in the same place as the word it defines in the already-finished quilt.

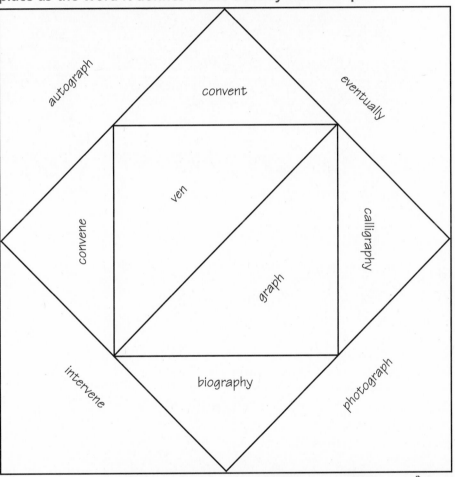

autograph

convent

eventually

convene

ven

calligraphy

graph

intervene

biography

photograph

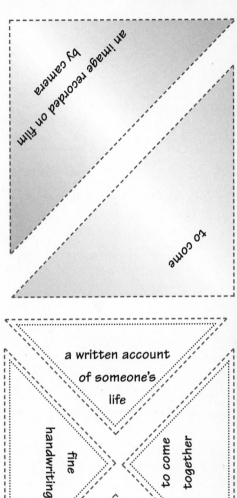

an image recorded on film by camera

to come

a written account of someone's life

fine handwriting

to come together

a building where nuns live

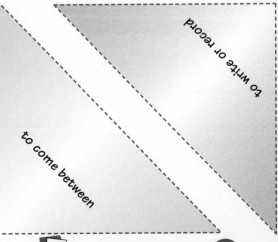

coming to be sooner or later

a signature in a person's own handwriting

to write or record

to come between

Name

Meaning Match

Find the word in the paint box on the right that belongs in the same category as a word in the paint box on the left. Color the matching circles.

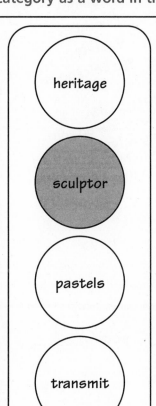

heritage

sculptor

pastels

transmit

realism

composition

dimension

Example:

a type of artist = gray

artist's materials = red

work of art = blue

other words for *communicate* = green

styles of art = yellow

other words for *a part of* = orange

something handed down = brown

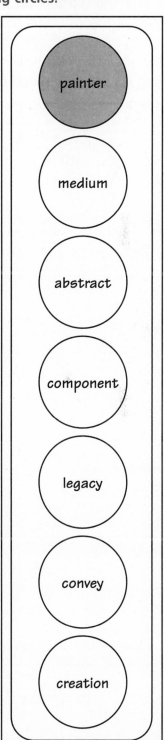

painter

medium

abstract

component

legacy

convey

creation

Name

Quilt Story Endings

Plurals of Words Ending with *o*

Each Spelling Word is the plural form of a noun
ending with **o**.

Form the plural of a noun ending with a vowel + **o** by
adding -**s**. Form the plural of a noun ending with a
consonant + **o** by adding -**s** or -**es**.

	Vowel + *o*	**Consonant + *o***	
Singular:	studio	solo	hero
Plural:	studios	solos	heroes

Form the plural of each word in the borders of the story quilt
by writing -*s* or -*es* beside the word. Then write each Spelling Word
below the correct heading.

Vowel + *o*

1 _____

2 _____

3 _____

Consonant + *o*

4 _____

5 _____

6 _____

7 _____

8 _____

9 _____

10 _____

echo_____   studio_____   potato_____

piano_____   stereo_____

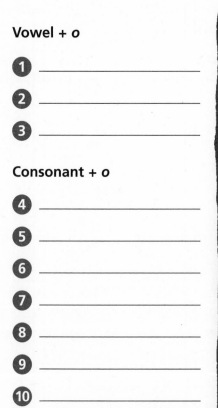

volcano_____   motto_____   solo_____

radio_____   hero_____

Spelling Spree

Analogies   Write the Spelling Word that completes each analogy.

Spelling Words

1. heroes
2. studios
3. radios
4. potatoes
5. mottoes
6. solos
7. pianos
8. echoes
9. stereos
10. volcanoes

1. scientists are to laboratories as artists are to _____

2. explosions are to bombs as eruptions are to _____

3. scrambled is to eggs as mashed is to _____

4. video jockeys are to television as disk jockeys are to _____

5. together is to alone as duets are to _____

Proofreading   Find and circle four misspelled Spelling Words in this review. Then write each word correctly.

Last night, the City Art Museum lived up to one of its motoes: "Put on a great show." The opening of the art exhibit on African American heros was spectacular. In the lobby, jazz musicians playing piannos greeted visitors. In many galleries, sterios played the music of famous blues and gospel singers as people viewed the outstanding art. Even the eckoes of the music in the hallways were thrilling.

6 _____

7 _____

8 _____

9 _____

10 _____

Story Quilt Titles   Faith Ringgold's idea to publish her stories on her artwork was imaginative. What stories might you tell on a story quilt? On a separate sheet of paper, write several titles for story quilts you might make. Capitalize important words in each title. Use Spelling Words from the list.

Name

Complete a Quilt

Adjectives	*what kind*	The **big** painting is **colorful**.
	how many	There are **many** colors in **one** painting.
Demonstrative	*which one*	I like **that** painting over there.
adjectives	*which ones*	He prefers **these** quilts right here.
Articles		**The** quilt tells **a** story with **an** illustration.

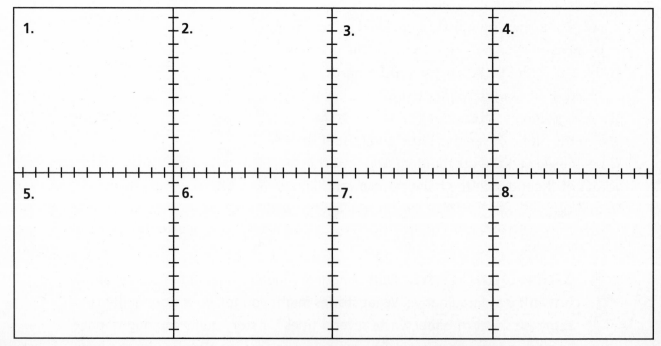

Adjectives Match each numbered type of adjective in the sentences with an adjective of the same type from the box. Write the adjectives in the quilt squares.

I am making (1. article) (2. what kind) quilt.
I will paint (3. how many) (4. what kind) decorations.
The design of (5. which one) quilt will be (6. what kind).
Perhaps someday people will know me as (7. which one)
(8. what kind) artist.

several	unusual
a/an	delightful
famous	this
colorful	that

1.	2.	3.	4.
5.	6.	7.	8.

Name

Fancy Stitches

Adjectives
Discover the hidden word. Color the boxes containing words that go with the article, demonstrative adjective, or type of adjective at the beginning of each row.

the	quilt	paint	frame	■	face	art	story	■	sun	moon	king
an	artist	brush	animal	green	eagle	young	idea	cow	crowd	owl	fish
a	museum	apple	picture	ink	bird	insect	flower	umbrella	ostrich	child	oyster
this	color	plates	room	peas	hand	sisters	fabric	beans	pigs	canvas	lines
these	colors	beads	people	fork	eyes	paintings	borders	dress	house	toes	ribbon
that	man	ribbon	table	boys	sculptor	shape	dogs	pants	cities	box	baskets
those	women	book	glasses	girl	pages	ear	spoons	button	shirt	windows	frame
what kind	large	two	loud	machine	joyful	weather	bridge	purple	ten	sad	bean
how many	three	blue	some	salty	forty	lucky	sunny	many	rainy	fifteen	tall

The hidden word is _____.

On a separate sheet of paper, write three sentences, using words from the chart in each sentence.

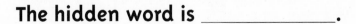

Imagination at Work 169

Name

Out of Print

Complete the television reporter's notes about a popular novelist with
the correct words.

revisions unexpectedly manuscript	desperate resort patiently

The crowd stood calmly and _____

outside. The bookstore hadn't opened yet, but the owner

knew that their patience would not last. He was sure that

they would _____ to breaking down

the doors if he didn't open them soon. He made a

last-minute, _____ search for the

missing author. To everyone's amazement, the author of

the book appeared _____ at the front

door. People in the crowd began shouting questions. They

wanted to know how long it took her to write the popular

novel. The author was happy to answer questions about

her book. "I completed the _____ in

only two months," she explained. "My editor only made a

few _____. One year later it's a

bestseller!"

Name

Snake Tails

Based on your understanding of *The Moon and I*,
add a tail—or ending—to each sentence to make it true.

1 The narrator is unhappy at the beginning because she cannot find _____

_____

_____

2 Sometimes, when the narrator can't decide how to begin a

chapter, she goes to the library. There she _____

_____

_____

_____

3 When the narrator is stumped, she "becomes the reader,"

which means she _____

_____

_____

_____

4 The narrator decides to let her character Nicole live after

she talks to _____

_____

_____

_____

_____

Imagination at Work **171**

Name

Editor's Eye

You are an assistant fiction editor. Read the story excerpt. Then use the
chart to help you determine the author's viewpoint.

> I couldn't think of a thing to write. My teacher had given us
> the assignment two weeks ago.
>
> "I want each of you to use your imagination for this
> assignment. Just picture what it would have been like to have
> sailed with Columbus, and write about it," she said.
>
> I was doomed to fail. Try as I might, I couldn't imagine what
> it would be like to sail across the ocean in search of a new
> route to India. My pencil just sat on the page, unmoving, until I
> dropped it on my desk.

Author's Viewpoint
What is the subject of the selection?
What point of view does the author use?
How would you describe the author's distance from the subject?
What is the author's attitude toward the subject?

On a separate sheet of paper, rewrite the excerpt. Use a different point
of view, distance from the subject, and attitude.

172 Imagination at Work

Name ....

Tell All About It

Help this author complete a chapter in her book by adding
adjectives to the sentences.

The Adventure Begins

The first day of our camping trip was _____

and _____. After kayaking all day on the

_____ river, we were all _____.

We ate dinner quickly, and then we lay by the

_____ fire and listened to the river. It sounded

so _____, I fell asleep immediately.

The next morning I awoke at sunrise. I had never seen a

sky so _____. Walking down to the

_____ pool in the rocks, I discovered along the

shore a bunch of wildflowers. They were _____

with _____ petals. They smelled

_____ and reminded me of something I couldn't

quite name. The water was _____ and

_____. It felt so _____ to take a

dip! As I floated on my back I could see on the horizon the

_____ mountain we would climb that day.

"Won't the view be _____ from up there," I

said to myself. Just then I heard the _____ cry

of a bird. Above me a red-tailed hawk soared. I knew then it

was going to be a _____ day!

Name

Writer's Block

Writers often brainstorm ideas before they begin to write. One idea sometimes leads to another. What word does each group of words below make you think of? Choose a word from the snake and write it in the blank.

script   inscribe

passport

postscript

reporter

1 ticket agent, pilot, baggage handler _____

2 actor, stage, curtain _____

3 Egypt, documents, parchment _____

4 suitcase, ticket, currency _____

5 meteorologist, sportscaster, cameraperson _____

6 doodle, sketch, scrawl _____

7 print, carve, engrave _____

8 greeting, body, salutation _____

porter   scribes   scribble

Name

Swirling Words

Read the clues. Then fill in the words on the snake's scales.

1 changes in your writing to make it better

2 surprising way some books end

3 to do something when nothing else works

4 opening sentence or paragraph

5 frustrated or without hope

6 what you do to get new ideas

7 finished work you send to your publisher

8 how you wait in a calm way

resort
revisions
manuscript
unexpectedly
desperate
lead
brainstorm
patiently

Name

Snake Sort

The Prefixes *dis-*, *mis-*, and *ex-*

Each Spelling Word begins with the prefix **dis-**, **mis-**, or **ex-**. A **prefix** is a word part that is added to the beginning of a base word or a word root. It adds meaning to the word.

Spelling Words

1. example
2. discontinue
3. expect
4. experience
5. distance
6. dissolve
7. disease
8. misspell
9. misunderstand
10. mischief

My Study List
What other words do you need to study for spelling? Add them to My Study List for *The Moon and I* in the back of this book.

PREFIX	MEANING	WORD	MEANING
dis-	not, opposite of	discontinue	opposite of *continue*
mis-	badly, wrongly	misspell	spell wrongly
ex-	out, out of	example	something picked out as a model

The base words or roots of several Spelling Words are given on each snake. On each snake's head, write the prefix that correctly completes the Spelling Words. Then write each Spelling Word under the correct prefix.

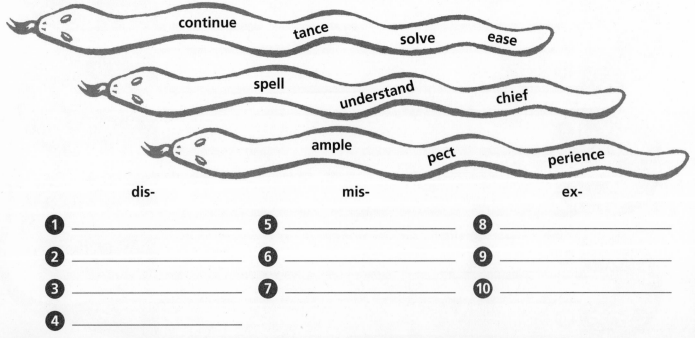

continue   tance   solve   ease

spell   understand   chief

ample   pect   perience

dis-   mis-   ex-

1 _____   5 _____   8 _____

2 _____   6 _____   9 _____

3 _____   7 _____   10 _____

4 _____

176 Imagination at Work

Name ....

Spelling Spree

Proofreading Find and circle four misspelled Spelling Words in this paragraph. Then write each word correctly.

> People often missunderstand snakes. The blacksnake, for exampel, is perfectly harmless to humans. It does not carry poison or disease. Do not expeck a blacksnake to be friendly, however. It will travel quite a distants if you come near it!

<table>
<tr><td>**Spelling Words**</td></tr>
</table>

Spelling Words

1. example
2. discontinue
3. expect
4. experience
5. distance
6. dissolve
7. disease
8. misspell
9. misunderstand
10. mischief

1 _____

2 _____

3 _____

4 _____

Slithery Dithering Write the Spelling Word that fits each clue.

5 naughty behavior
— — — — — — — —
                    7

6 to stop
— — — — — — — — — —
      8   4

7 to have something happen to oneself
— — — — — — — — — —
            1

8 to spell incorrectly
— — — — — — — —
            3   6

9 to change from a solid to a liquid
— — — — — — — —
      5

10 illness
— — — — — — —
                  2

Now write the numbered letters in order to complete this statement.

The blacksnake is one of about 6,000 kinds of __ __ __ __ __ __ __ __.

Writer's Block Betsy Byars tells of several ways she stirs her imagination when she has writer's block. What do you do when you can't think of how to begin a piece of writing? When you don't know what to write next? On a separate piece of paper, write a few pointers of your own for dealing with writer's block. Use Spelling Words from the list.

Name

Question and Answer

Is a blacksnake **longer** than a garter snake?

Is a snake a **worse** pet than a dog?

Comparing with Adjectives   Write the correct form of each adjective in the puzzle. Then find and color a hidden word that tells something all writers use.

Interviewer: What part of writing is the ___1___ of all for you? (hard)

Writer: Getting an idea often is the ___2___ part for me. (difficult)

Interviewer: Do you spend ___3___ time planning than writing? (more)

Writer: It is ___4___ of all for me to work out a general plan first. (easy)

Interviewer: What is one ___5___ way to think of an idea? (good)

Writer: One of the ___6___ ideas of all came from a pet. (interesting)

Interviewer: Are writers ___7___ than people think? (energetic)

Writer: Writing can be ___8___ than riding a bicycle! (active)

Interviewer: When is the ___9___ time of all for you to write? (good)

Writer: I am the ___10___ in the early morning. (inspired)

Interviewer: What makes one book ___11___ than another? (popular)

Writer: Even the ___12___ writer wonders about that! (fine)

Name

Picture Forms

Comparing with Adjectives

Use your imagination to write and illustrate adjectives. Use one adjective that adds *-er* and *-est*, one that adds *more* and *most*, and one irregular adjective.

Adjective	**Comparative Form**	**Superlative Form**

Example: leafy   leafier   leafiest

1

_____   _____   _____

2

   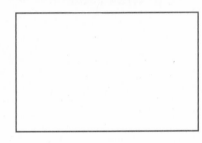   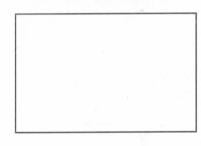

_____   _____   _____

3

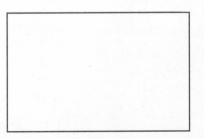

_____   _____   _____

What Do You Think?

Essay Topics **Does one of these topics suggest an essay idea to you?**

Clouds	Reading
Broccoli	What Makes Me Happy
The Right/Wrong Pet	A Holiday I Hate
Studying	Being Fair
Growing Up Isn't Easy	Looking on the Bright Side
Choosing the Right Shoes	

My Personal Essay Topics

Write five ideas that you might like to write about in a personal essay.

_____

_____

_____

_____

_____

Ask yourself these questions about each idea you listed.

Can I think of good examples to explain my thoughts?

Do I really want to write about this?

Do I have interesting points to make?

Now circle the topic that you will write about.

180 **Imagination at Work**

Name

Put on Your Thinking Cap

Use this diagram to plan your essay. Write your focus idea in
the center. Around it list your thoughts about your focus idea.
In the outside circle, add examples to support each thought.

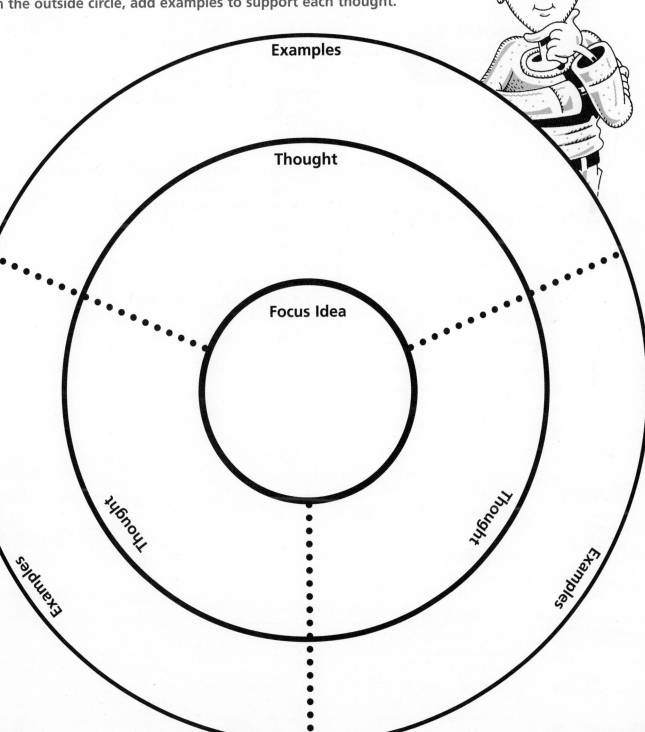

Examples

Thought

Focus Idea

Thought

Thought

Examples

Examples

Does It Work?

Reread and revise your essay, using the Revising Checklist. Then use the Questions for a Writing Conference to help you discuss your essay with a classmate.

Revising Checklist

☐ Does the opening present the focus idea?

☐ Do all my points and thoughts keep to the focus idea?

☐ Did I use good examples to explain each point or thought?

☐ Does the closing sum up the focus idea and make the essay seem finished?

Questions for a Writing Conference

- What do you like about this essay?
- Is the opening interesting? Does it clearly state the focus idea?
- Does each point or thought keep to the focus of the essay?
- Do the examples clearly explain each point? Should different examples be used? Are more examples needed?
- What parts are unclear?
- Could the closing be improved?
- What other revisions might be helpful?

Write notes to help you remember comments and suggestions made during your writing conference.

My Notes

_____

_____

_____

_____

_____

_____

_____

Name

Getting It Right!

Use these words to fill in the missing pieces of one of the Wright brothers' recollections of their work in Kitty Hawk.

tedious

accuracy

stabilize

systematic

calculations

absorbed

data

The problem we faced was this: How do we design the glider so that it will fly steadily? We were determined to find a way to _____ it. We were all so _____ in the research project that it was all that interested us. Even when the work got _____, it wasn't because it was boring, but because it took so much time. We had to be very organized because there was so much _____ to gather and make sense of. We conducted our research as all scientists do, in a very

_____ way, following an orderly process. Each time we built and operated a new test model, for example, we would closely observe its performance in all sorts of wind conditions and record the results. All the careful thinking and planning and making all those _____ required all our attention. Since each of us really had to focus, there was little time or room for distractions. We found joy and delight in getting the right results. We strove for _____, for work free from all error.

....
Name

Pilot's Log

Fill in the missing words in Orville Wright's logbook.

1901: We have just begun to compile data in the workroom behind our

_____. To test wing surfaces

under different air pressures, we have decided to build a

_____. We are sure this will

enable us to make the correct calculations for designing a

_____ that will really take off!

1902: August We have relocated to _____

_____, along North Carolina's coast. We discovered that our

_____ had been battered

by _____! We have

decided to _____ it.

September Our new glider is the biggest ever. We launch it from the top of Big

Hill, then practice _____

_____ as it glides down. To steer the glider right or

left, we _____

the wings. This causes one wing to tip up while the other tips down,

thus making the glider turn in the direction of the _____

_____ wing.

Name _____

Don't Just Wing It!

What were three problems and solutions that the author presented to organize information about the Wright brothers? Each cloud gives you a clue.

Calculations

Problem: _____

_____

Solution: _____

_____

Airfoil

Problem: _____

_____

Solution: _____

_____

Tailspin

Problem: _____

_____

Solution: _____

_____

 Imagination at Work

Name _____

Getting Organized

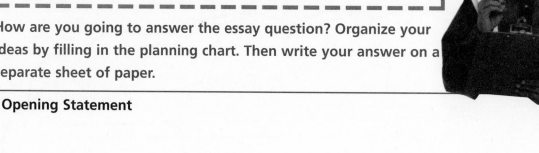

Question: How did Wilbur and Orville's experiments with the wind tunnel show that they were creative, patient, and curious?

How are you going to answer the essay question? Organize your ideas by filling in the planning chart. Then write your answer on a separate sheet of paper.

Opening Statement

Details to Support the Opening Statement

Closing Statement

Name

Creature Comforts

This student interviewed her family to find out their favorite inventions. Write the words in each response that contain the prefixes *ad-*, *con-*, *in-*, *ob-*, or any of their other spellings. The numbers tell you how many words there are in each response.

My Survey Results

1 My brother Eric likes headphones because he can listen to music without aggravating our parents. They don't object to the loud volume or to his music choice anymore.   *(2)*

_____

2 My sister Emma is a university student. She voted for the laptop computer. It allows her to accomplish work while riding the train to school. She claims it's made the typewriter obsolete.   *(4)*

_____

_____

3 Dad says he depends on his car phone to communicate with clients while he drives to and from work. I told him to pay more attention to the road if he wants to avoid having a collision!   *(3)*

_____

4 Mom says she really appreciates the convenience of wearing contact lenses. She used to misplace her glasses constantly before switching to lenses.   *(4)*

_____

_____

5 My grandfather was always an incredible photographer. But recently he bought a video camera and hasn't touched his old camera since! Grandpa says the video camera is the best invention of the century. He jokes about going to Hollywood someday!   *(2)*

_____

   Imagination at Work

Name _____

Inventive Lists

Think about what it takes to be an inventor. Then complete
each list with words from the box and with your own words.

**Things You Need to
Get Good Results**

observations

_____

_____

_____

_____

**Words That Describe the
Invention Process**

repetitious

_____

_____

_____

_____

**Problems That
Need to Be Solved**

flight performance

_____

_____

_____

How You Might Feel

excited

_____

_____

_____

_____

Name

Words on the Wing

The Prefixes *per-*, *pre-*, and *pro-* Each Spelling
Word begins with the prefix *per-*, *pre-*, or *pro-*.

Prefix	Meaning	Word
per-	through, thoroughly	perfect
pre-	before, in front	prepare
pro-	forward, before	process

**Add the prefix *per-*, *pre-*, or *pro-* correctly to each base
word or word root on the glider wings. Then write
each Spelling Word under the correct prefix on the
sand dunes.**

Spelling Words

1. prepare
2. process
3. perform
4. problem
5. perfect
6. propose
7. persist
8. preview
9. profession
10. prehistoric

My Study List
What other words do you
need to study for spelling?
Add them to My Study List
for *The Wright Brothers* in the back
of this book.

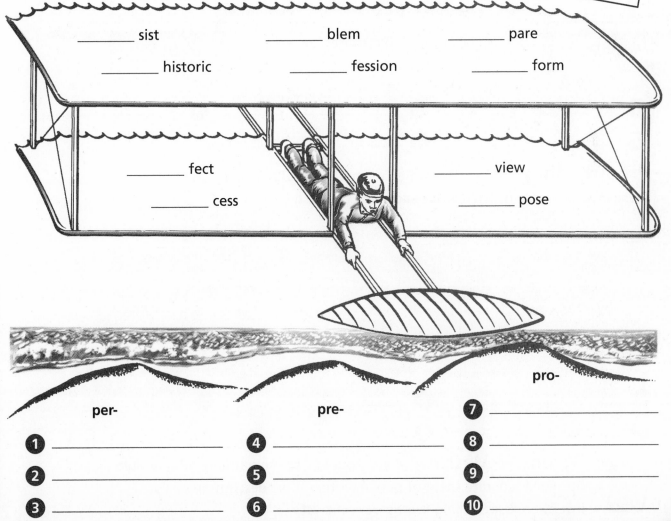

_____ sist   _____ blem   _____ pare

_____ historic   _____ fession   _____ form

_____ fect   _____ view

_____ cess   _____ pose

per-

1. _____
2. _____
3. _____

pre-

4. _____
5. _____
6. _____

pro-

7. _____
8. _____
9. _____
10. _____

Name _____

Spelling Spree

Headlines of 1902   Write a Spelling Word to replace the underlined word or words in each newspaper headline.

Spelling Words
1. prepare
2. process
3. perform
4. problem
5. perfect
6. propose
7. persist
8. preview
9. profession
10. prehistoric

1. Brothers <u>Get Ready</u> for Test Flight

2. Reporters Get <u>Advance Showing</u> of Amazing Invention

3. Discovery of <u>Extremely Ancient</u> Bones Eclipsed by Events in Kitty Hawk

4. Wrights Explain <u>Series of Steps</u> They Use to Fly

5. Wright Brothers <u>Suggest</u> New Invention

1 _____   **3** _____   **5** _____

2 _____   **4** _____

Proofreading   Find and circle five misspelled Spelling Words in these inventor's notes. Then write each word correctly.

My invention does not *preform* as well as I had hoped. A major *problam* has arisen. If it should *presist*, my hopes will be dashed. I will continue, though, to search for the *perfict* solution to my dilemma. With luck, in a few weeks I will be able to give others in my *perfession* a preview.

6 _____   **8** _____   **10** _____

7 _____   **9** _____

Inventive Writing   If you could invent something, what would it be? On a separate sheet of paper, write a short description of your invention. Use Spelling Words from the list.

Name

Negative Notes

Incorrect: The Wright brothers **didn't never** stop with the success of their glider.

Correct: The Wright brothers **didn't** stop with the success of their glider.

Avoiding Double Negatives   A reporter wrote these sentences about the Wright brothers' first successful airplane flight on December 17, 1903. Rewrite the sentences, correcting the double negatives.

1 The brothers would not let no fear hold them back.

_____

_____

2 Weather conditions weren't no good that windy day.

_____

_____

3 The Wright brothers didn't hardly postpone the flight.

_____

_____

4 Orville could not barely hear the cheering people.

_____

_____

5 There hasn't never been anything like this historic flight!

_____

_____

The Airplane–An Unlikely Idea?

Avoiding Double Negatives The Wright brothers worked without success for a long time. Write five objections you think people might have had to the idea of a powered airplane, and write five answers to the objections. Use one negative word in each sentence.

OBJECTION	ANSWER
Example: The idea of flying won't ever work!	→ Nothing is impossible!
1	→
2	→
3	→
4	→
5	→

Planning an Invention

Invent a machine you would like to have. Think of a problem your machine could solve, such as tying your shoes or cleaning your room. Your invention doesn't have to be realistic. Be specific about how your invention will fulfill its duties and what parts it will need to make it work. Fill out the information below to plan your invention.

Problem: _____

_____

Solution: _____

_____

Describe exactly how your machine will solve your problem.

_____

_____

_____

List the parts your machine will need to fulfill its function.

1 _____   **5** _____

2 _____   **6** _____

3 _____   **7** _____

4 _____   **8** _____

On another sheet of paper, draw a diagram of your machine to show how it works. Label all the parts of your machine. Give your diagram a title that indicates what your invention does. Make your diagram as clear and easy to understand as possible.

Share your invention with your group. Explain why it is realistic or why it is not.

> Use this checklist to decide if you're ready to share your invention.
> ❏ I have invented a machine that solves a problem.
> ❏ My diagram is easy to understand.
> ❏ I can explain why my invention is realistic or not.

Name

Finding Common Ground

In each of the selections in this theme, characters overcome differences and find common ground. Use the chart below and on the next page to compare and contrast selections.

	Pacific Crossing	The Wrong Lunch Line
Who are the main characters?		
How are they different?		
What experience brings them closer together?		
What "common ground" do they discover as a result?		

Name

Finding Common Ground

In each of the selections in this theme, characters overcome differences and find common ground. Use the chart to compare and contrast selections.

	Shiloh	The Pinballs
Who are the main characters?		
How are they different?		
What experience brings them closer together?		
What "common ground" do they discover as a result?		

Name _____

Sports Flash!

Use all five vocabulary words to complete this newspaper article.
You may use a word more than once.

| dedicated | executed | meditation | practitioners | tournament |

See page 2 for
scoreboard.

SPORTS JOURNAL   May 15

Martial Arts on the Move

The Fifth Annual Karate _____ will be held this weekend in the Kyoto Studio at 520 Elm St. _____ from around the state will be competing for a chance to attend the international competition in Japan next fall.

The _____ begins at 9:00 A.M. on Saturday. If you wish to participate in the opening _____ and observe the opening ceremonies, arrive a half hour earlier.

_____ of karate are some of the most _____ athletes around. Expect to see hand positions and leg kicks _____ with great skill and grace. Plan to arrive early and bring a lunch, as the _____ continues without a break throughout the day.

Terrific Pacific TV

Imagine that *Pacific Crossing* is being considered for an after-school TV special. Summarize what happens in the three scenes.

SCENE 1: *Outdoors. A back street in a Japanese town.*

SCENE 2: *Interior. Mitsuo's home. Family having tea.*

SCENE 3: *At the dojo.*

Name

Reading Between the Lines

Check your understanding of what is really happening in *Pacific
Crossing.* Circle the number of each statement that is a correct
inference. Then complete the equations to support the inferences.

1. Mitsuo helps Lincoln feel at home.
2. Baseball is not a popular sport with the Ono family.
3. Lincoln does not miss his father.
4. Occasionally, Mitsuo misunderstands what Lincoln says.
5. Mrs. Oyama is a good teacher.

Story Clues +	**Personal Experiences** =	**Inferences**

Addressing an Envelope

To address an envelope properly, you must have a main address and a return address. The **main address** provides the name and address of the person receiving the letter. The **return address** provides the name and address of the sender.

Lincoln Mendoza
899 Pierce St.
San Francisco, CA 94115 **return address**

USA

Jackson Anderson
2121 East 86th Pl.
Apartment 2B
Chicago, IL 60617 **main address**

Remember to do these things, or your letter may not reach its destination.

• Be sure the ZIP Code is correct. The Postal Service workers look at the ZIP Code, not the town.

• Be sure to include apartment numbers as well as street addresses. Add the names of the countries if you are mailing to another country.

• Be sure your handwriting is readable!

• Attach the correct postage.

Address this label. Use your address for the return address. Write the address of someone you know for the main address.

Extra! You can find all ZIP Codes in the U.S. Postal Service's ZIP Code Directory. Look up and write the ZIP Codes for these places.

1 The White House,

Washington, D.C. _____

2 Big Cottonwood Canyon Rd.,

Salt Lake City, UT _____

3 Put In Bay, OH _____

4 1202 78th Ave., Miami, FL _____

Name

What's the Meaning of This?

**You're part of a linguistic team that has discovered a new
language on a remote island in the Pacific. Your team has found
the meaning of all the words except the four italicized ones.
Study the words in context and then fill in the chart.**

The high mountain peaks rose into the *yamusonir*. The sun shone brightly but
the air was so *borkuf* that all of the backpackers wore gloves and scarves.
From high up, they could see the *nidugyk* playing in the ocean waves below.
Their fins glistened in the sunlight as they jumped from the water. After a
while, since everyone was tired, the climbers stopped by a pond to *turike*.

WORD	PART OF SPEECH	CLUES FROM CONTEXT	MY BEST GUESS AT MEANING
yamusonir			
borkuf			
nidugyk			
turike			

Name

Tips for Karate Students

Based on what you've learned about karate from *Pacific Crossing*, use these words to write ten tips for karate students.

dedicated	executed
meditation	practitioners
tournament	concentrate
considerate	progress
instructors	techniques

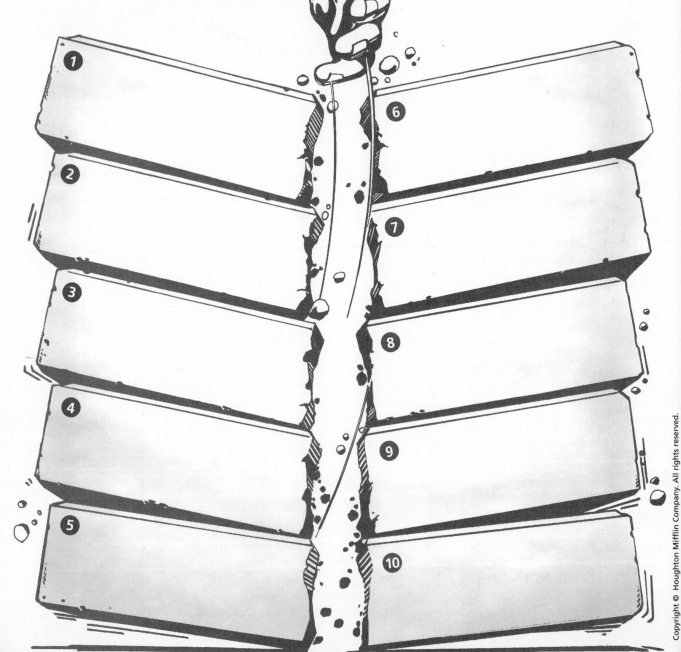

Across the Pacific

Words that End with *-ize* or *-ise* Each
Spelling Word has the final sounds in **realize**, shown
as līzl. These sounds can be spelled with the pattern
ize or *ise*. Words that end with *-ize* or *-ise* are
usually verbs.

līzl   rea**liz**e exer**cis**e

Draw a line from each base word or root to the
ending that makes a word. Then write the
Spelling Words under the correct endings.

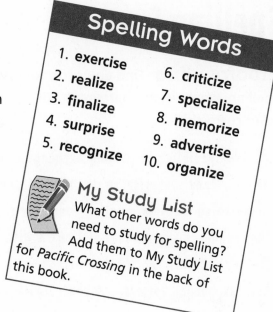

Spelling Words
1. exercise
2. realize
3. finalize
4. surprise
5. recognize
6. criticize
7. specialize
8. memorize
9. advertise
10. organize

My Study List
What other words do you
need to study for spelling?
Add them to My Study List
for *Pacific Crossing* in the back of
this book.

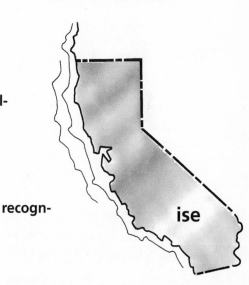

JAPAN

surpr-

memor-

exerc-

real-

final-

critic-

advert-

organ-

recogn-

special-

ize

CALIFORNIA

ise

-ize		-ise
❶ _____	❺ _____	❽ _____
❷ _____	❻ _____	❾ _____
❸ _____	❼ _____	❿ _____
❹ _____		

Name

Spelling Spree

Proofreading
Find and circle four misspelled Spelling Words in this paragraph. Then write each word correctly.

We spesialize in placing exchange students in Japan. Many a suprise awaits these students because we organize so many interesting tours for them. Also, we reelize that students worry about fitting in with their host families. Because of this, we finelize arrangements only after students have exchanged letters and photos with their Japanese families.

1 _____

2 _____

3 _____

4 _____

Travel Tips
Write Spelling Words to complete these tips for exchange students.

5. Before your trip, try to ____ a few basic phrases in the language of your host country.

6. If your passport, visa, and other travel documents aren't in order, ____ them.

7. To help avoid jet lag after your arrival, ____ moderately before you board the plane.

8. Study photos of your host family before you land, so you will ____ them at the airport.

9. After you arrive, remember not to ____ the customs of your host family.

10. Last but not least, try not to ____ the fact that you're nervous!

5 _____

6 _____

7 _____

8 _____

9 _____

10 _____

 First Day in Japan Imagine that, like Lincoln, you have just spent your first day in Japan as an exchange student. On a separate sheet of paper, write a journal entry describing your day. Use Spelling Words from the list.

Name

Baseball Banter

Subject and Object
Pronouns
Mitsuo wants
to learn more words about his
favorite game, baseball. Add
subject and object pronouns to
these explanations of baseball
words. Remember to capitalize
the first word in a sentence.

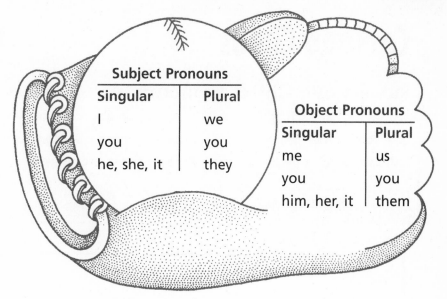

Subject Pronouns	
Singular	Plural
I	we
you	you
he, she, it	they

Object Pronouns	
Singular	Plural
me	us
you	you
him, her, it	them

WARM-UP

Muscles get stiff. Ballplayers must be sure to exercise

(they/them) _____ before a game.

(They/Them) _____ may hit balls, for instance.

A warm-up is good for all of (we/us) _____ .

BULLPEN

Since a pitcher must warm up his arm, (he/him) _____

needs a practice place. Someone helps (he/him) _____ ,

tossing the ball to (he/him) _____ .

(They/Them) _____ throw the ball back and forth in the

bullpen. That word interests (I/me) _____ .

DUGOUT

When we players are not on the field, (we/us) _____

need a place to sit. There is a dugout for (we/us) _____ . It is

low, but (I/me) _____ can still see the field.

SHORTSTOP

The shortstop is important. (She/Her) _____ stands

between second and third base. Anyone can throw the ball to

(she/her) _____ . Also, it is (her/she) _____ who

protects the infield.

**On a separate sheet of paper, write an explanation of a special term from a
sport that you enjoy. Use at least one subject pronoun and one object pronoun.**

Name

Cartoon Chaos

Subject and Object Pronouns Find out what these people
are saying. In each speech balloon, write an appropriate pronoun from the
box. Remember to use a capital letter to begin a sentence. In the last
balloon, write a response using at least three pronouns.

you	she	them	it	her	he	we	I	they	us	me	him

Did _____ see Adam at the dojo? _____ was with Lee, and both of _____ were practicing.

No, _____ didn't see _____. Someone was there, but it wasn't _____. _____ will go tomorrow. Maybe he'll join _____.

_____ learned some side kicks. Watch _____. Then tell me what you think of _____.

_____
_____
_____

Name _____

Behavior Banter

You're teaching a friend to play charades, a game in which you act out the meanings of words without speaking. To help your friend get started, write suggestions for how to act out the meaning of each word.

anxiously: Pretend you're getting ready to take a test, waiting for the teacher to say "Begin!" and you're really nervous.

1 reassurance _____

_____

_____

2 nonchalantly _____

_____

_____

3 suppressed _____

_____

_____

4 persisted _____

_____

_____

5 impulsively _____

_____

_____

Name

What's for Lunch?

Think of a menu as "what happens" in a meal. Now think of this selection as three meals. For each "meal," list three menu items (events) by completing the sentences.

MĚNU

· ·

BREAKFAST   Getting in Line

Juice   Yvette decides to join Mildred in the line for Passover lunches.

Main Course   Elba _____

Vitamin   A teacher asks Yvette _____

_____

LUNCH   Humiliation

Salad   The teachers ask Yvette _____

Main Course   They send her to _____

Dessert   The vice-principal says _____

_____

DINNER   After School

Salad   Yvette and Mildred_____

Main Course   Together, they eat _____

Dessert   When they mention Mrs. Ralston,_____

_____

A Story of Friendship

Imagine that you've been asked to write a story that shows the value of friendship. In the chart, describe two characters, a place and time, and a plot. Then, in the frame, draw or describe a picture that represents the most exciting moment in your story.

CHARACTERS

Name _____

Brief Description _____

Name _____

Brief Description _____

SETTING

Time _____

Place _____

PLOT

Problem _____

Turning Point _____

Resolution _____

Name

The Same but Different

Use the Venn diagram to help you compare or contrast the details of the XYZ School
lunchroom with the same features of your school's lunchroom. Then write
a paragraph of comparison and contrast on a separate sheet of paper.

> The XYZ School lunchroom has long tables lined up end to end with metal folding
> chairs on either side. There are no windows, just wide fluorescent lights all over the
> ceiling. Some of the pipes on the ceiling are exposed, but they are painted green, just like
> the cinder-block walls. On one wall is a mural, painted by students, that shows the woods
> and the playground behind our school. The floor is tan linoleum, always scuffed up. It's
> only shiny after school vacations. The lunchroom always smells like chicken soup.

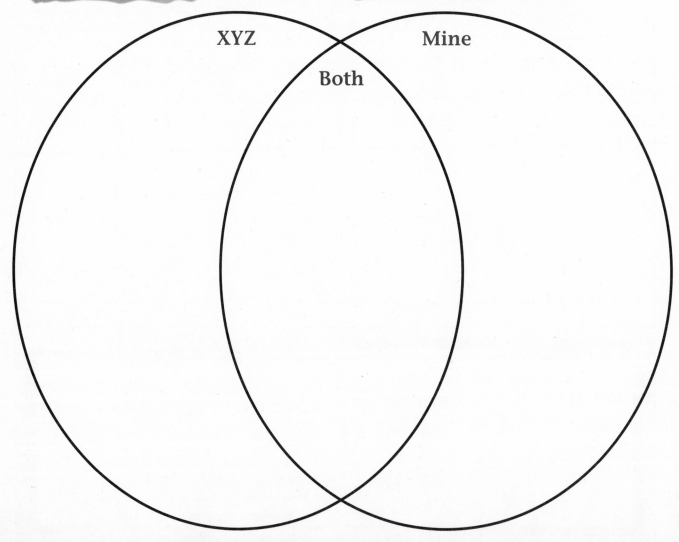

XYZ   Mine

Both

No, Thanks!

Each meaning is followed by a string of letters.
Each string of letters contains two synonyms that
use negative prefixes. Circle the two words.

1 NOT ALIKE: disdissimilarsiunequal

2 NOT MAJOR: miunimportantlainsignificantrit

3 NOT PLEASANT: iunfriendlyedisagreeables

4 NOT ACCORDING TO THE RULES: arunlawfuleuillegalni

5 NOT TELLING THE TRUTH: mpdishonestorinsinceretan

6 NOT ARRANGED: tidisorderlyntounorganizedle

7 NOT EASY TO GET TO: rainconvenientnunreachablecei

8 NOT ABLE TO BE DONE: suimpossiblenaundoablecce

9 NOT FOLLOWING ORDERS: pdisobedienttuncooperativeab

10 NOT CARING: lenonchalantnunconcernedon

11 NOT LINKED: counrelatedndisconnectedfo

12 NOT ABLE TO BE COUNTED ON: rundependablemisirresponsiblets

13 NOT NEEDED: shirrelevantouunnecessaryld

14 NOT CALM OR ACCEPTING: beimpatientunintolerantas

15 NOT CEASING: hunendingamnonstoped

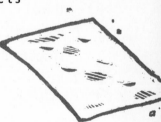

Now look back at the letters you did not circle. Write them
in order on the lines below to make three sentences that
express three possible themes of "The Wrong Lunch Line."

1 _____

2 _____

3 _____

 Finding Common Ground **211**

Name _____

Crossly Worded

Use the words to complete the crossword puzzle.

anxiously	encouragement	nonchalantly	suppressed	cautiously
impulsively	persisted	convulsively	nervously	reassurance

Across

2. In an unconcerned or carefree way

4. Opposite of "in an impulsive manner"

9. Act of restoring confidence

10. In a tense or jumpy way

Down

1. In an eager or worried way

3. The act of inspiring hope

5. Suddenly; without thinking or planning

6. Insisted or repeated stubbornly

7. In a sudden, uncontrolled way

8. Held back or kept in

Name

Matzo Tidbits

Words That End with *-ant* or *-ent*

Each Spelling Word ends with ***-ant*** or ***-ent***, shown as
|ənt|. These patterns sound alike. Because the spelling
of the schwa sound is not clear, you must remember
the spellings ***-ant*** and ***-ent***. Words that end with ***-ant***
or ***-ent*** are usually adjectives or nouns.

|ənt| pleasant   different

Complete each Spelling Word by adding *-ant* or
-ent to each word part. Then write each Spelling
Word below the correct pattern.

Spelling Words

1. different
2. pleasant
3. ignorant
4. patient
5. moment
6. frequent
7. important
8. student
9. vacant
10. brilliant

My Study List

What other words do you
need to study for spelling?
Add them to My Study List
for *The Wrong Lunch Line* in the
back of this book.

brilli_____   frequ_____   pleas_____   vac_____

differ_____   ignor_____   import_____

stud_____   pati_____   mom_____

-ant

1 _____
2 _____
3 _____
4 _____
5 _____

-ent

6 _____
7 _____
8 _____
9 _____
10 _____

Name

Spelling Spree

Radio Days Write the Spelling Word that is an antonym of each underlined word in this radio script.

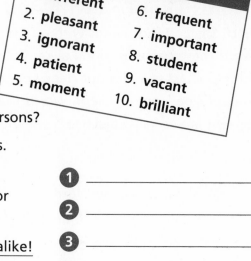

Spelling Words

1. different
2. pleasant
3. ignorant
4. patient
5. moment
6. frequent
7. important
8. student
9. vacant
10. brilliant

Mr. Keene: (*phone rings*) I'd better get the phone. This call could be <u>insignificant</u>. Hello?

Caller: Is this Mr. Keene, the <u>dull</u> tracer of lost persons?

Mr. Keene: Yes, I've been called that on <u>rare</u> occasions. How can I help you?

Caller: Well, I may have a <u>disagreeable</u> surprise for you. It's about that kid you're looking for.

Mr. Keene: Hey, I'll listen to anything that's new and <u>alike</u>! I don't have a single lead on that case. What have you got?

Caller: You know the <u>full</u> building at . . . Oh, no! (*caller screams*)

Announcer: Tune in next week for more adventures of Mr. Keene, tracer of lost persons.

1 _____
2 _____
3 _____
4 _____
5 _____
6 _____

Proofreading Find and circle four misspelled Spelling Words in this note. Then write each word correctly.

Your daughter, Yvette, is usually a pleasant and cooperative studdint. However, she recently acted up in the lunchroom, pretending to be ignarant of the school rules on special free lunches. Now, I am a pacient person. For the momant, I am willing to go easy on her. If Yvette acts up again, though, I will have to take firm action.

7 _____
8 _____
9 _____
10 _____

Fair or Unfair? What do you think of rules on separating free-lunch and bag-lunch students? What do you think of the way the teachers treated Yvette? Write your opinion of one of these topics. Use Spelling Words from the list.

Name _____

All Together Now

Pronouns in Compound Subjects and Objects

Help Yvette finish these sentences in her journal by writing the correct pronouns. Circle the letter in the column on the right that shows whether you wrote a subject pronoun or an object pronoun.

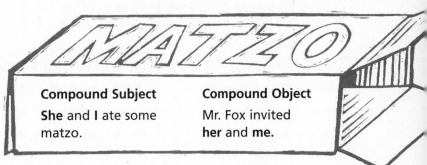

Compound Subject	Compound Object
She and **I** ate some matzo.	Mr. Fox invited **her** and **me**.

	Subject Pronouns	Object Pronouns
Mildred and _____ wanted the Passover lunch. (I, me)	C	B
_____ and the other students went to the (We, Us) lunchroom.	H	L
The teachers guided _____ to the lunch lines. (us and them, them and we, them and us)	Y	I
Usually _____ and Elba eat with the others. (she, her)	C	A
The vice-principal spoke to the other class and _____. (we, us)	R	K
Some teachers questioned _____. (she and I, her and me, I and she)	O	E
_____ just wanted to eat together. (She and I, Her and me, Me and her)	N	B
Mr. Fox said the incident did not embarrass his wife or _____. (he, him)	P	S
Later, _____ invited me to dinner. (him and her, he and she)	O	T
We ate with my family and _____. (they, them)	X	U

Write the circled letters in order. You'll find another food that might be eaten on Passover.

___ ___ ___ ___ ___ ___   ___ ___ ___ P

The Right Birthday Party

Pronouns in Compound Subjects and Objects

Yvette is having a birthday party! Because she wants people to have fun, she has asked her friends about their likes and dislikes. Read their notes and write five sentences to help plan the party. Yvette has written one. Use pronouns, including *I* and *me,* in compound subjects and objects.

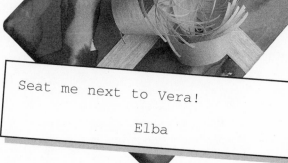

Musical chairs sounds good to me—
to Maia and Mildred too.
Beth

Seat me next to Vera!
Elba

*I love to dance –
so do Keesha and Elba.*
Karen

REMEMBER, NO MEAT FOR ME.
MILDRED

How about frankfurters and milk?
Maia

*I hate hot dogs and hamburgers.
I want to sit with Elba.*
Jocelyn

Franks! Hamburgers! Ice cream! Milk!
Keesha

I want to sit next to Maia and Beth.
Vera

Example: I'll get vegetable pizza for Mildred, Jocelyn, and me.

_____

_____

_____

_____

_____

Word Families

Use the dictionary to find two kinds of related words for these vocabulary words. In the middle box, list words that are closely related in meaning. In the third box, draw or paste a picture that you think shows the meaning of the word. Use a dictionary, a thesaurus, or a partner to help you.

WORD	WORDS RELATED IN MEANING	IMAGE
suspicions		
mistreat		
obliged		

In the Doghouse

Ever hear the expression "in the doghouse" to describe someone who is in trouble? At various points in the selection, each character faces important decisions. Fill in the chart with what you consider the characters' most important choices and decisions. Notice that what you write in the two middle columns are facts. What you write in the last column is your opinion.

CHARACTER	CHOICE	DECISION	RIGHT OR WRONG?
Marty			
Ma			
Dad			
Doc Murphy			

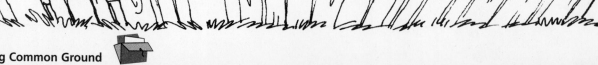

Clues to Judgment

Choose the two judgments from the list
that are supported by story clues in
Shiloh. Write each judgment in the
chart. Then list at least two story clues
that support it.

1. Marty's father values telling the truth.
2. Marty's father values obeying the law.
3. Marty's father is a cruel man.
4. Marty's father is a sad man.

JUDGMENT

STORY CLUES

The Right Dog for You

Suppose you edit a booklet describing available pets at an animal shelter. Make this description more interesting to read by moving the underlined words in five sentences. (Be careful not to change the meaning of a sentence.) Use circles and arrows to show the moves. Then write your revised paragraph, using capital letters correctly.

Example: Visit an animal shelter when you want a pet.

When you want a pet, visit an animal shelter.

This adorable mongrel puppy can be yours with one simple phone call! Duke is about eight or nine months old. He will be a medium-sized dog when fully grown. His shiny fur is dark brown except for one small patch of white at the tip of his tail. Duke plays with small children gently. He is calm and well behaved inside the house, but he is quite playful outside. Duke even knows how to catch a tennis ball in his teeth! Duke came to the shelter because his owner could no longer care for him. He needs to find a new home quickly. Please call right away if you're interested.

_____

_____

_____

_____

_____

_____

_____

_____

Name _____

Shiloh Is to Dog . . .

Read this analogy.

Secret is to unspoken as treasure is to <u>buried</u>.

    valuable   buried   whisper   mystery

The answer is buried because a secret is hidden by being unspoken, and a treasure is hidden by being buried.

Write the word that best completes each analogy.

1 Flower is to daisy as tree is to _____.
    pine   tall   perfumed   green

2 Hammer is to pound as needle is to _____.
    nail   thread   sharp   stitch

3 Fingernail is to claw as hand is to _____.
    dog   hold   paw   foot

4 Happy is to content as angry is to _____.
    pleased   smile   frown   grouchy

5 Question is to answer as problem is to _____.
    agree   obey   solution   easy

6 Coin is to nickel as bill is to _____.
    paper   metal   money   dollar

7 Tear is to eye as blood is to _____.
    wound   bandage   leg   red

8 Fight is to quarrel as bite is to _____.
    nip   snarl   swallow   attack

These words could appear in analogies. Use them to write two incomplete analogies and challenge a partner to complete them.

tail	family	temperature	human	thermometer
shout	pack	temperament	bark	dog

9 _____

10 _____

 Finding Common Ground 221

....

Name

What About Shiloh?

Use the vocabulary words to continue the dialogue between Marty
and Judd Travers. Use the vocabulary words in the box. Read your
completed dialogue aloud with a partner.

suspicions   mistreat   obliged   grateful   evidence   compassion   canine   abuse

Marty: I want to keep Shiloh. I can take care of him better than you.

Judd: _____

_____

Marty: _____

_____

Judd: _____

_____

Marty: _____

_____

Judd: _____

_____

Marty: _____

_____

Judd: _____

_____

Marty: _____

_____

Judd: _____

_____

Name

Shiloh's Escape

Words That End with *-ance* or *-ence*

Each Spelling Word ends with *-ance* or *-ence*, shown as
|əns|. These patterns sound alike. Because the spelling
of the schwa sound is not clear, you must remember
the spellings *-ance* and *-ence.* Words that end with
-ance or *-ence* are usually nouns.

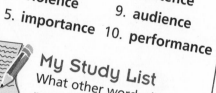

|əns| allowance   silence

My Study List
What other words do you
need to study for spelling?
Add them to My Study List
for *Shiloh* in the back of this book.

Help Shiloh reach the house. Draw a line that
connects each incomplete Spelling Word to the correct ending.
Then write each Spelling Word under its ending.

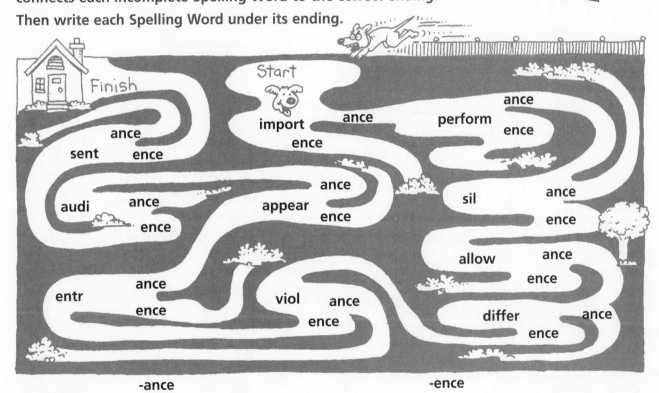

-ance

1. _____
2. _____
3. _____
4. _____
5. _____

-ence

6. _____
7. _____
8. _____
9. _____
10. _____

Spelling Spree

Analogies Write the Spelling Word that completes each analogy on Doc Murphy's kitchen table.

Spelling Words

1. silence
2. difference
3. allowance
4. violence
5. importance
6. appearance
7. entrance
8. sentence
9. audience
10. performance

1 Runner is to race as actor is to _____.

2 Light is to dark as similarity is to _____.

3 Bricks are to house as words are to _____.

4 Sing is to performer as listen is to _____.

5 Departure is to arrival as exit is to _____.

6 Ear is to sound as eye is to _____.

Proofreading Find and circle four misspelled Spelling Words in this pet-care guide. Then write each word correctly.

- Keeping your pet clean is of the utmost importence.
- Never use any kind of viollence on a pet. Make an allowince for normal, frisky behavior.
- Good veterinary care can make all the difference in the world to a pet's health.
- Loud noises startle many pets. Be sure your pet has some restful times of silents.

7 _____   **9** _____

8 _____   **10** _____

Righting Wrongs Marty learned that many animals are mistreated by people. Make some posters protesting animal abuse. Use Spelling Words from the list.

Who's Who?

Using *who, whom, whose* Judd Travers has hired a pet detective to try to find his dog. Here are some of the questions the detective asks. Complete them by writing the correct pronoun in the blank. Remember to use a capital letter when the pronoun begins a sentence.

who — subject

whom — object

whose — possessive

1 _____ has seen a strange dog today? (Who, Whom)

2 _____ is the brown spotted dog? (Whose, Who's)

3 _____ footprints are in the yard? (Whose, Who's)

4 _____ did you see near Judd's house yesterday? (Who, Whom)

5 _____ does not have an alibi for yesterday afternoon? (Who, Whom)

6 _____ does the dog often visit? (Who, Whom)

7 From _____ did Judd buy the dog? (who, whom)

8 _____ witnessed anything unusual in the area yesterday? (Who, Whom)

9 _____ leaving fingerprints on the doorknob? (Whose, Who's)

10 _____ should I question next? (Who, Whom)

11 For _____ is that box of dog cookies? (who, whom)

12 _____ has lost a dog recently aside from Judd? (Who, Whom)

13 _____ is that empty doghouse? (Whose, Who's)

14 _____ saving food scraps? (Whose, Who's)

15 _____ found the dog? (Who, Whom)

To Whom It May Concern

Using *who, whom, whose* Follow the instructions stated in the memo.

MEMO

To: Title Tellers, Inc.
From: Shiloh Products

We need your help! The story of Shiloh has become so popular that everyone is talking about following it up with a new book about Marty and Shiloh. A New York publisher wants to use it, and so do many other publishers around the world. They have great ideas, but they cannot think of good book titles.

Please help by writing six possible book titles for a sequel. You must use the words *who, whose, who's,* or *whom* at least once in each title. Remember to capitalize the first, last, and each important word in a title and to underline your titles.

1 _____

_____

2 _____

_____

3 _____

_____

4 _____

_____

5 _____

_____

6 _____

_____

My Opinions and Goals

Topic Ideas

What goals of your own do these suggestions make you think of?

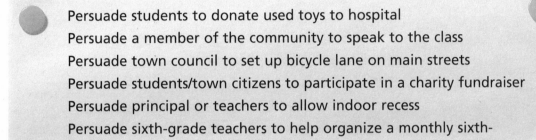

Persuade students to donate used toys to hospital

Persuade a member of the community to speak to the class

Persuade town council to set up bicycle lane on main streets

Persuade students/town citizens to participate in a charity fundraiser

Persuade principal or teachers to allow indoor recess

Persuade sixth-grade teachers to help organize a monthly sixth-grade after-school social activity

My Ideas Write five goals you have for persuading someone to do something.
Next to each goal, name the audience you need to persuade.

What   **Who**

_____   _____

_____   _____

_____   _____

_____   _____

_____   _____

Now ask yourself these questions about each goal.
Then circle the topic that you will write about.

Do I really care about this?

Can I reach an audience who can do something about it?

Do I have strong reasons with facts and examples to support the goal?

Do I know enough about this?

Finding Common Ground **227**

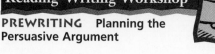

Be Convincing!

Complete the persuasion web to help you plan your argument.

Reason

Facts/Examples

Reason

Facts/Examples

Opinion

Audience

Goal

Reason

Facts/Examples

Objection

Answer

Name

Make It Stronger

Reread and revise your persuasive argument, using the Revising
Checklist. Then use the Questions for a Writing Conference to
help you discuss your persuasive argument with a classmate.

Revising Checklist

☐ Did I state my opinion and goal clearly?

☐ Did I give strong reasons?

☐ Did I support each reason with convincing facts and examples?

☐ Did I answer possible objections?

☐ Did I handle each reason and objection separately?

☐ Did I introduce and conclude my argument effectively?

Questions for a Writing Conference

• What do you like about this persuasive argument?

• Are the opinion and the goal clear?

• Which reasons are convincing, and which ones are unconvincing? Why?

• Where are stronger or additional facts or examples needed?

• Will the answers to the objections satisfy the audience?

• Do the introduction and conclusion help make the argument memorable?

Write notes to remember ideas discussed in your writing conference.

My Notes

_____

_____

_____

_____

Name

What's Going On?

When you find yourself in a new situation, sometimes it's hard to describe what's going on. Use two of the situations described below to tell about each verb. Then add a third situation from your own experience or from something you've read about.

A mountain climber wouldn't use a thin rope that she thought was weak.

I paused before I reached for a third helping of potatoes.

An advertisement said that a laundry detergent removed any stain.

A driver stopped at a stop sign, then drove into the intersection.

I wouldn't be on your team because you had made fun of me before.

That girl announced that she was the best pinball player in town.

List three situations that illustrate the verb **hesitated.**

1 _____

2 _____

3 _____

List three situations that illustrate the verb **claimed.**

4 _____

5 _____

6 _____

List three situations that illustrate the verb **distrusted.**

7 _____

8 _____

9 _____

Name

Three by Three

Think about the three young characters in *The Pinballs.* Each one has a past and a present in the story—two parts of their lives that they are trying hard to put together. In the chart describe each character's past and present. Use the third column to write what you hope they will make of their futures.

	PAST	PRESENT	FUTURE
Carlie			
Thomas J			
Harvey			

Name

An Editor's Hat

You are a newspaper editor reviewing a story about foster kids. Rewrite the overgeneralizations so they are "narrowed down." For each generalization, write two details from *The Pinballs* that support it.

Example: All foster kids tell lies to protect their feelings.

Some foster kids tell lies to protect their feelings.

1. Harvey lies about how his legs were broken.

2. Carlie makes up stories about her birth and infancy.

GENERALIZATION: Foster kids always have someone they trust.

_____

1 _____

2 _____

GENERALIZATION: All kids who become foster kids are in physical danger.

_____

1 _____

2 _____

GENERALIZATION: Every foster family can offer every kid protection and hope.

_____

1 _____

2 _____

Name

Dear Diary

Read Carlie's diary entry. Circle any nouns that are repetitive. Replace them with pronouns. Underline pronouns that are unclear. Replace them with the nouns they refer to. Write the new nouns and pronouns over the words they replace.

Dear Diary,

I knew this place was going to be trouble from the second I saw Mrs. Mason on Mrs. Mason's front porch. She had on an apron and was trying to look like a perfect mother. The social worker and Mrs. Mason said they would be arriving later that afternoon. I asked her questions about the two boys, but she would only tell me the two boys' names were Harvey and Thomas J. I met them soon after. He has two broken legs. He yells all the time. They are already driving me crazy. Thomas J used to live with two old ladies, and Thomas J got used to speaking loudly because the two old ladies were hard of hearing.

I feel pretty crummy. She told me the first night's always the hardest. I hope she's right.

Choose two pronouns that you replaced. Explain why you replaced them and how you decided which words to replace them with.

_____

_____

_____

_____

_____

Name

Look Away

Use the word grids to put together words with the roots *tele* and *vis/vid*. To build words, move from square to square, adding syllables as you do. Write each word after its meaning. Use a dictionary if necessary.

in	ad	en
e	VIS	it
ion	ible	or

Example: someone who helps you see clearly by giving an opinion   **advisor**

1 part of a cap that protects the eyes _____

2 not able to be seen _____

3 a person who goes to see someone or something _____

pro	super	tape
VISE	VID	o
ence	ent	e

4 picture portion of a television broadcast _____

5 magnetic material used for recording and playing images _____

6 obvious; easy to see _____

7 to be in charge of; oversee _____

vise	scop	path
phone	TELE	ic
course	met	ry

8 capable of seeing distant objects _____

9 able to read someone else's mind _____

10 a device that sends and receives speech _____

Name _____

Pinball Wizard

Write the words from the box that have the same meaning as the words in bold type. Use a dictionary if necessary.

paused
contended
doubted
faltered
flinched
insisted
disbelieved
asserted
suspected

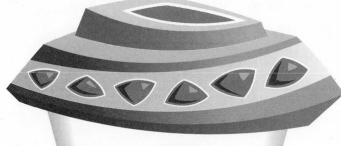

claimed

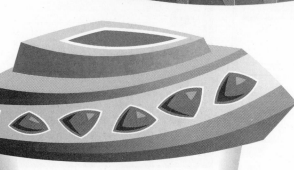

distrusted

hesitated

Name

Family Photos

Words That End with *-able* or *-ible*

Each Spelling Word ends with the suffix *-able* or *-ible*. Because the spelling of the schwa sound in the suffix is not clear, you must remember the spelling patterns.

Suffix	Meaning	Word
-able, -ible	capable of	lovable possible
	worthy of	
	tending toward	

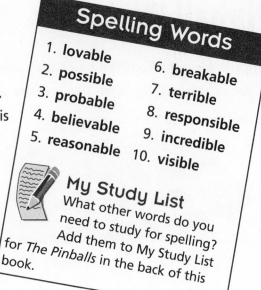

Spelling Words

1. lovable
2. possible
3. probable
4. believable
5. reasonable
6. breakable
7. terrible
8. responsible
9. incredible
10. visible

My Study List
What other words do you need to study for spelling? Add them to My Study List for *The Pinballs* in the back of this book.

Help Mrs. Mason label the children's photos. Draw a line to connect each photo to the correct suffix to form the ten Spelling Words. Then write each Spelling Word under the matching suffix.

poss

break

terr

lov

-able

reason

vis

-ible

respons

believ

incred

prob

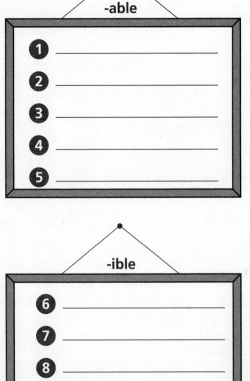

-able

1 _____
2 _____
3 _____
4 _____
5 _____

-ible

6 _____
7 _____
8 _____
9 _____
10 _____

Name

Spelling Spree

Proofreading Find and circle five misspelled
Spelling Words in this social worker's report. Then
write each word correctly.

> **Spelling Words**
> 1. lovable
> 2. possible
> 3. probable
> 4. believable
> 5. reasonable
> 6. breakable
> 7. terrible
> 8. responsible
> 9. incredible
> 10. visible

Carlie is a very responcible young woman.
She also has increadible strength of character. However,
because of probile mistreatment as a young child, she has a
terrible mistrust of everyone. I think it is quite possable that over
time, Carlie can become a very loveable person.

1 _____   **3** _____   **5** _____

2 _____   **4** _____

What Is the Question? Carlie was a big TV fan. Write a Spelling
Word to finish each question on this TV game show.

Multi-Syllable Words

6 This word and *dreadful* share their meaning. What is _____ ?	**8** A statement that is worthy of trust is this. What is _____ ?	**10** This word is a synonym of *fragile*. What is _____ ?
7 This word means "sensible" or "logical." What is _____ ?	**9** This word describes stars on a clear night. What is _____ ?	

Cast Creativity Harvey was upset because no one had autographed
his casts. On a separate sheet of paper, compose some messages that you
might write on Harvey's casts. Use Spelling Words from the list.

Name

Definitely TV Time

Indefinite Pronouns

Carlie might enjoy a puzzle
about TV. Write the verb form
that fits each sentence. Then
write the indefinite pronoun
subject in the puzzle.

SINGULAR
Someone watches TV.

PLURAL
Both watch TV.

Across

2. All of today's shows _____ listed in the paper. (is/are)

4. Everything _____ to be a talk show. (seems/seem)

5. Nobody at our house _____ talk shows. (watches/watch)

7. Anything good _____ us to the TV set, though. (draws/draw)

Down

1. Everybody _____ to like quiz shows. (seems/seem)

2. Anyone with a little knowledge _____ eligible. (is/are)

3. Few of my friends _____ much TV. (watches/watch)

6. Many of them _____ busy with other things. (is/are)

Word Bonus Now, for a bonus, use an indefinite pronoun to write a slogan that fits the theme Finding Common Ground.

_____

_____

Who Watches What?

Indefinite Pronouns A polling company has taken a survey of the TV viewing habits of one hundred people. The chart shows which programs they watched and how many TV sets they owned. Write sentences below, using information from the chart. Use present tense forms of the verbs from the TV box to agree with the indefinite pronoun subjects given.

prefer	like
watch	enjoy
look	choose
select	be
have	own

Survey Results
(100 people surveyed)

Program Types	Viewers	TV Sets in Home	Viewers
talk shows	33%	1	100%
quiz shows	71%	2	65%
dramas	81%	3	14%
comedies	80%	4	1%
sports	75%	more than 4	0%
news	100%		
late-night shows	28%		

1 Some _____
2 Others _____
3 Few _____
4 Someone _____
5 Everybody _____
6 Many _____
7 Nobody _____
8 Everyone _____
9 Several _____
10 Somebody _____

Name
_____

Planning a Playground

Imagine that your community is planning a playground for children up to age twelve. The available space is about four times as big as a basketball court. It can have grass surfaces, hard surfaces, or a mixture. It can have lights for use in the early evening. How would you plan the playground?

Here are some things to remember as you plan.
- The playground is for children of different ages.
- Even children of the same age enjoy different things.
- There will probably need to be rules or regulations for using the playground.
- Most important: the purpose is for all children to have a good time.

What facilities, or objects, should the playground have?

_____

_____

_____

How should things be arranged? On a separate sheet of paper, draw a map. What rules or regulations should there be? List just a few—the ones that you think would be especially useful or helpful.

1 _____

2 _____

3 _____

4 _____

5 _____

Finally, even if you have an excellent plan, other people will have other ideas. How should a group of people go about making a final plan?

_____

_____

_____

 LIST

❏ I have a plan for the playground facilities and where they should be.

❏ I have a helpful list of rules and regulations.

❏ I have suggestions on how people could agree on a final plan.

Ocean Quest

The ocean is the source of all life on our planet, and a world in itself. A quest is a search, an expedition, or a journey for something precious or valuable. Consider the meaning of the theme as you complete the chart below and on the next page.

	Oceans	The Search for the Right Whale
Describe one thing you discovered about the ocean in this selection.		
Was there any sense of a quest in this selection? Explain.		
Explain what sort of movement or action took place in this selection.		
How did this selection affect your perception or knowledge of ocean life?		

Name

Ocean Quest

The ocean is the source of all life on our planet, and a world in itself. A quest is a search, an expedition, or a journey for something precious or valuable. Consider the meaning of the theme as you complete the chart.

	After the Spill	Joel Rubin
Describe one thing you discovered about the ocean in this selection.		
Was there any sense of a quest in this selection? Explain.		
Explain what sort of movement or action took place in this selection.		
How did this selection affect your perception or knowledge of ocean life?		

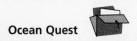

Name

Dear Professor Alba Tross

As you read the letter to a scientist at Woods Hole Oceanographic Institute, use context clues to fill in the missing vocabulary words.

currents	rotates	gravitational	moderates	evaporates	condenses

Dear Professor Alba Tross,

I enjoyed the class visit to Woods Hole. I learned how the

_____ pulls of the moon and the sun create tides.

I never knew that as the earth _____ each day,

two high tides and two low tides occur. The ocean is more important

to weather than I realized, too. I didn't know that when ocean

_____, such as the Gulf Stream, travel from warm

regions to cooler ones, they affect the climate. So that's why palm

trees can grow along certain coasts in Ireland. It's sort of amazing

how the North Pacific Current _____ temperatures

on the California coast!

I like the way the planet recycles water! I think it's really cool the

way salt water _____ from the ocean into the sky

and then it _____ and falls back as rain or snow.

But I still can't figure out where the salt goes.

Thank you for taking the time to show us around the institute.

Sincerely,

Star Fish

Name

Motion Commotion

Complete the flow chart about *Oceans* to show three major
topics and three of their subtopics.

OCEANS

Ocean Motion

currents	tides	waves

On a separate sheet of paper, make your own flow chart. Choose
another subject and break it down into topics and subtopics.

Ocean Odyssey

Ocean life falls into three main categories—plankton, nekton, and benthos. Read the description of each category.

> **Plankton**—small or microscopic plants and animals that float
> **Nekton**—animals that swim freely, including fish and mammals
> **Benthos**—plants and animals that live on or near the ocean floor

Using reference materials and your knowledge of the ocean, classify these plants and animals into one of the categories.

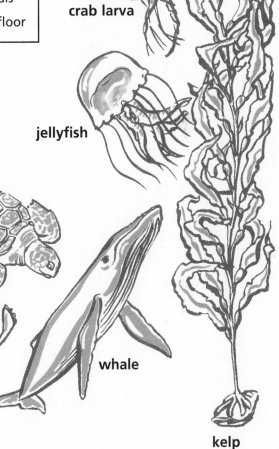

diatoms

crab larva

jellyfish

loggerhead turtle

giant squid

whale

kelp

oyster

starfish

Plankton	Nekton	Benthos

Name

Simply Add Details

Elaborate the message on this post card by adding adverbs.

We arrived on Friday afternoon and have been
_____ swimming and fishing! The sun has
been shining _____ since our arrival!
_____ we went on a whale watch cruise
and spotted two humpback whales swimming
_____ in the bay. This morning I woke up
_____ and watched the sun rise. I heard
a noise _____ and saw a mongoose walking
_____ across the lawn. Later, we sat
_____ on the beach and then walked until
we _____ reached the lighthouse. I
_____ wish you were here!

_____

_____

_____

Now write a second post card to the same person. Describe events that occurred after
you wrote the first post card. Use at least one adverb in each sentence.

_____

_____

_____

_____

_____

_____

_____

stamp
here

_____

_____

_____

Name

The High Seas

Use the words on the pen to complete this diary entry written by an unhappy traveler.

conspiring
currency
transpired
respiratory
incurring
spirits
perspiration
excursion

Somewhere at Sea
August 1995

Dear Diary,

Why did I ever sign up for this dreadful _____ to the islands? You wouldn't believe what has _____! Our boat ran into high winds, which are causing very rough seas. Now everybody is suffering from sea sickness, and _____ are generally low. On top of all that, my allergies have been causing me _____ problems. I simply lie on my bed in my stuffy

cabin, my clothes drenched in _____, dreaming of the mainland. I've stopped ordering anything from room service because I'm afraid of _____ too many expenses; I only have about twenty dollars of foreign _____ left! Some of the passengers are _____ to jump ship at the next port of call, and fly back on the first flight available. I may be home sooner than expected.

Name ....

Catch of the Day!

Write a vocabulary word for each definition.
When you are done, the circles will form a word.

| evaporates | condenses | currents | moderates | gravitational | rotates |

1 changes from a liquid to a vapor

2 movements of water

3 keeps within reasonable limits

4 having to do with the force of attraction

5 becomes concentrated

6 turns around on an axis

The catch of the day is the word: _____ _____ _____ _____ _____ _____

Fill in the word web. Use the vocabulary words and what you've learned about oceans.

Ocean _____ flow for thousands of miles.

Ocean water _____ into the air.

Oceans

A warm current _____ a cool climate.

The _____ pull of moon and sun causes tides.

Name

Word Waves

The Prefix *in-* Each Spelling Word begins with the prefix *in-*. The prefix *in-* can mean "**without, not,**" as in *incomplete* or "**in, within, or into,**" as in *include*. The prefix *in-* is usually spelled *im* before a base word or a word root beginning with *m* or *p*.

No Spelling Change

in + complete   = incomplete
in + clude   = include

Spelling Change

in + mense   = immense
in + port   = import

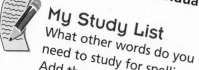

Spelling Words

1. immense
2. include
3. import
4. involve
5. impossible
6. immediate
7. inquire
8. incomplete
9. immigrant
10. individual

My Study List
What other words do you need to study for spelling? Add them to My Study List for *Oceans* in the back of this book.

Write the correct spelling of the prefix *in-* on each wave to complete each Spelling Word. Then write each word in the column with the matching prefix.

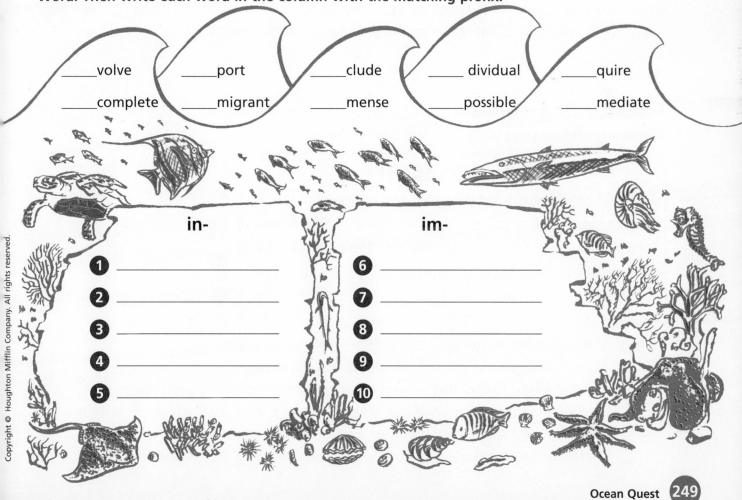

_____volve   _____port   _____clude   _____dividual   _____quire

_____complete   _____migrant   _____mense   _____possible   _____mediate

in-   im-

1. _____   6. _____
2. _____   7. _____
3. _____   8. _____
4. _____   9. _____
5. _____   10. _____

Name

Spelling Spree

Spelling Words
1. immense
2. include
3. import
4. involve
5. impossible
6. immediate
7. inquire
8. incomplete
9. immigrant
10. individual

Tidal Wave! Write the Spelling Word that fits each clue.

1 to make someone or something part of a group

— — — — ▢ — —

2 a person who leaves one country and settles in another

— — — — — — ▢ — —

3 not capable of happening

— — — — ▢ — — — —

4 to bring goods in from another country

▢ — — — ▢ —

5 not finished

▢ — — ▢ — — — — —

Now unscramble the shaded letters to make a word that answers this question: What is the Japanese word for "tidal wave"?

Answer: ____ ____ ____ ____ ____ ____ ____

Proofreading Find and circle five misspelled Spelling Words in this news bulletin. Then write each word correctly.

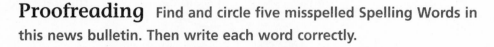

NEWS FLASH!!

We interrupt this program for some important news. An imense tidal wave is approaching. An evacuation order is in force for every individule in the coastal area. Because it is impossible for authorities to check every building, they request your immedeate departure. For information about whether the evacuation should envolve you, inquier at any police station.

6 _____

7 _____

8 _____

9 _____

10 _____

Save Our Oceans! Imagine that you are an oceanographer who is very troubled by the pollution of our oceans. On a separate sheet of paper, write the summary of a speech you might give to encourage people to take active roles in the cleanup of our oceans and beaches. Use Spelling Words from the list.

Name

How? Where? When?

how	The ocean <u>roared</u> **noisily**.
where	The ocean <u>roared</u> **outside**.
when	The ocean **always** <u>roared</u>.
to what extent	The ocean **really** <u>roared</u>.

Adverbs Read these items from a training handbook for oceanographers. Write the adverb in each sentence and underline the word it modifies.

1 Ocean water moves constantly. _____

2 Sometimes ocean currents shift. _____

3 Water temperatures change nearby. _____

4 Sea life almost disappears. _____

Choose an adverb from the box to complete each sentence. Remember to begin a sentence with a capital letter.

soon   there   swiftly   hardly

5 A tsunami moves across the ocean _____. (how?)

6 You _____ notice it in the ocean. (to what extent?)

7 _____ it approaches the shore. (when?)

8 _____ it hits with a powerful force. (where?)

Write four sentences about the ocean, using each adverb shown.

9 _____ (away)

10 _____ (usually)

11 _____ (carefully)

12 _____ (completely)

....
Name

Before It's Too Late

Modifies adjective ⟶ Ocean pollution is **quite** <u>serious</u>. ·
Modifies adverb ⟶ We must protect our oceans **more** <u>carefully</u>.

Adverbs Help this writer complete an editorial. In the first
paragraph, circle each adverb and underline the adjective or adverb it
modifies. Complete the second paragraph with adverbs from the box.

OCEAN ALERT

Ocean pollution is becoming increasingly serious. The
waters of the earth become dirtier almost daily. We must help our
oceans before it is too late. Without the sea, the earth would
become totally lifeless quite quickly. It is terribly important to
clean up our oceans.

Many people treat the ocean as an _____
large dump. Because cities _____ often pump their
waste into the sea, sewage is a _____ serious
problem. Ships _____ always dump their garbage
overboard.

totally
very
extremely
terribly
rather
nearly
particularly
increasingly
almost
really
quite
too

**Complete the editorial with two sentences of your own, using at least
two adverbs to modify adjectives or adverbs.**

_____

_____

_____

_____

_____

Name

Marine Mammal Mix-Up

Use a thesaurus to find a synonym and an antonym for each
vocabulary word.

	Synonyms	Antonyms
essential		
consolidate		
survey		
integrate		
distinctive		

Now cut out the pieces. Mix them up and turn them face down. Take
turns with a classmate turning over three cards at a time. If the cards do
not match, turn them back over. If they match, keep them. At the end of
the game, the player with the most cards wins.

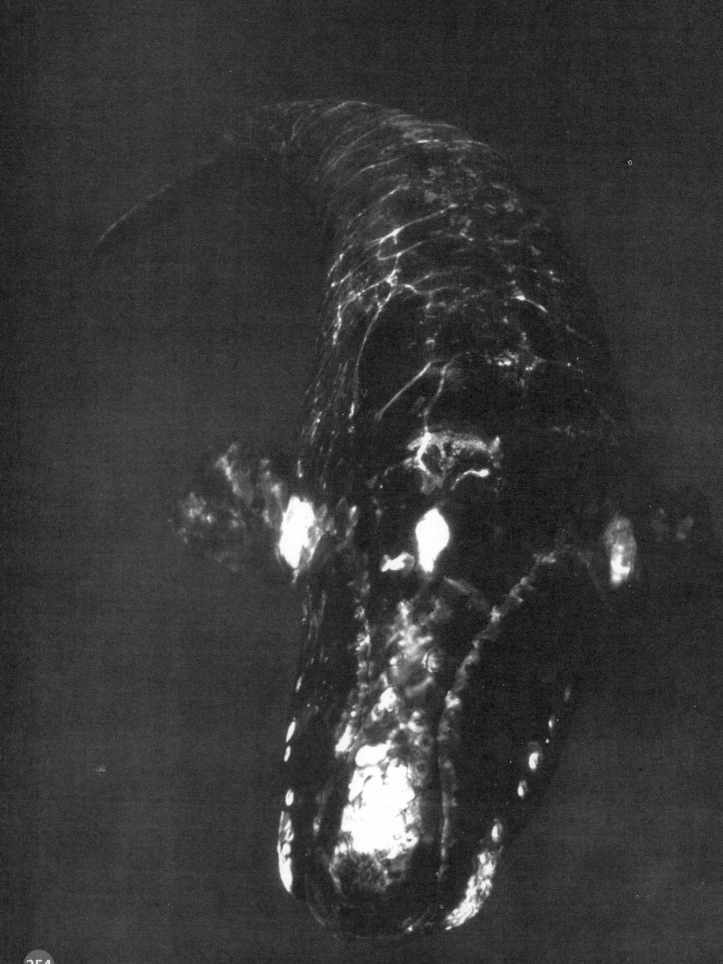

The Right Report

Fill out the chart about the survey on right whales. Use only
the facts in the selection.

- **WHO is completing the survey?**
- **WHAT is the survey about?**
- **WHERE did the survey take place?**
- **WHY was the survey started?**
- **WHEN did the survey take place?**
- **HOW did researchers perform the survey?**

WHO	WHAT
WHERE	WHEN
WHY	HOW

Name _____

Stars and Stripe Forever

Fill in the chart about the whales Stars, Stripe, and Forever.

	Stars	Stripe	Forever
Distinctive Markings			
Position in Family			
Behavior			

Use the information from the chart to answer the questions.

1 Which whales are most similar in their markings? _____

_____

2 Which whale looks most different from the others? _____

_____

3 How are the whales related to each other? _____

_____

4 What is similar about the whales' behavior? _____

_____

....

Name

Write All About It

Write a news article about something that happened in your
school or community. Try to talk to people who observed or
were involved in the event. Record facts about the event. If necessary,
check several sources to make sure your facts are correct.

What happened? _____

_____

Who was involved? _____

_____

When and where did the event take place? _____

_____

Why did the event take place? _____

_____

Other details: _____

_____

_____

_____

Quotations (include each person's name and his or her involvement): _____

_____

_____

_____

Now write a headline for your news article. Try to catch your readers' attention
with a few well-chosen words.

Headline: _____

Now write your news article on a separate sheet of paper. Give details about
the event. Try to include quotations from eyewitnesses.

....

Name

Surprise Visitors

Replace each underlined word with an antonym.

September 12, 1997

As our boat set out into the <u>icy</u>, <u>rough</u> seas this afternoon, we were <u>doubtful</u>
     1   2   3
that we'd have a sighting of the <u>rare</u> right whale. But, today we were
                                 4
<u>fortunate</u>. We spotted a right whale <u>floating</u> on the <u>surface</u> of the ocean with
5   6   7
her calf, and stopped to take some photos.

The mother had a <u>long</u>, white scar and <u>strange</u> patches of <u>rough</u> skin on her
                  8   9   10
<u>shiny</u> black head. She was a <u>powerful</u> swimmer and made <u>many</u> <u>deep</u> dives
11   12   13   14
in search of food. Her calf seemed <u>bored</u> and restless, but waited for its
                                    15
mother and didn't swim off. Mothers and calves <u>always</u> stay <u>close</u> <u>together</u>.
                                                16   17   18
The <u>timid</u> whales <u>never</u> came very close to our boat. We hope to catch up
    19   20
with the whales again tomorrow.

1 _____   8 _____   15 _____

2 _____   9 _____   16 _____

3 _____   10 _____   17 _____

4 _____   11 _____   18 _____

5 _____   12 _____   19 _____

6 _____   13 _____   20 _____

7 _____   14 _____

Name

Whale Word Webs

Use the words in the box to
complete the word webs.

examine	consolidate	essential
oceanic	crucial	nourishment
laborious	tedious	integrate
survey	unique	distinctive
marine		

put together

not like the others

take a close look at

badly needed

tiresome

from the sea

food

Name

Whale Words

The Prefix *con-*

Each Spelling Word has the prefix **con-**, meaning "together" or "with." The prefix **con-** is often spelled **com** before a base word or word root beginning with **b, m,** or **p.**

con + duct = conduct   con + mand = command
con + bine = combine   con + pare = compare

Add *con-* or *com-* to each word part to make a Spelling Word. Then write the word under the matching prefix.

_____mon   _____tinue

_____pany   _____cern

_____duct   _____vince

_____tain

_____bine

_____mand

_____pare

Spelling Words

1. command
2. conduct
3. convince
4. common
5. compare
6. contain
7. concern
8. combine
9. continue
10. company

My Study List

What other words do you need to study for spelling? Add them to My Study List for *The Search for the Right Whale* in the back of this book.

con-

1 _____
2 _____
3 _____
4 _____
5 _____

com-

6 _____
7 _____
8 _____
9 _____
10 _____

Name ....

Spelling Spree

Proofreading   Find and circle four misspelled
Spelling Words in this paragraph from a research
report. Then write each word correctly.

We began to conducked this survey with one
goal in mind. We wanted to be sure that right
whales continnue to increase in number. After our
study, we went on to conpare our findings with
those of other researchers. We were then able to
combine the results and draw conclusions. Happily,
those conclusions have eased our consern for the
fate of the North Atlantic right whale.

1 _____

2 _____

3 _____

4 _____

Synonyms at Sea   Write the Spelling Word that is a synonym
of the underlined word in each sentence.

5. Dad's <u>business</u> sponsored a whale-watching trip.
6. Captain Ahab had <u>authority</u> on our boat.
7. He said that an <u>ordinary</u> adult blue whale is almost
   100 feet long.
8. We learned that the mouths of bowhead whales <u>hold</u> a lot
   of baleen.
9. You don't need to <u>persuade</u> me to avoid a narwhal's spiral tusk!
10. My sister and I are going to <u>join</u> our allowances and buy
    a book on whales.

5 _____   8 _____

6 _____   9 _____

7 _____   10 _____

A Whale of a Day   Imagine that you are the captain of a research
boat. You are exploring the right whale's summer habitat in the Bay of Fundy.
Throughout the day, you and the research team have spotted a number of right
whales. On a separate sheet of paper, write the log entry you might make
after this exciting day. Use Spelling Words from the list.

Name ....

All Aboard the *Whale Wheel!*

ADVERB
This whale swims
fast,
quickly,
well.

COMPARATIVE
This whale swims
faster,
more quickly,
better.

SUPERLATIVE
This whale swims
fastest,
most quickly,
best.

Comparing with Adverbs *Whale Wheel* is a boat that takes
passengers on whale-watching trips. Here are statements the owner is
considering for a brief commercial. Write the correct comparing forms of
the adverbs. Then try writing two statements of your own for the ad,
using an adverb in a comparison.

1 The *Whale Wheel* sights whales _____ than any other boat.
(frequently)

2 Of all the boats, the *Whale Wheel* skims across the water _____.
(smoothly)

3 No boat gets _____ to the whales than the *Whale Wheel*.
(close)

4 Whom do we worry about _____ of all? The whales.
(much)

5 Our sharp-sighted crew can spot a whale _____ than others can.
(easily)

6 Our whale-watching trips are organized _____ than others.
(well)

7 On the *Whale Wheel*, you will sit _____ than in your own home.
(comfortably)

8 Compare the service on all the boats. Our crew treats you the _____ of all.
(well)

9 Of all trips, ours gets you there _____.
(fast)

10 Watch three whales leaping. Which will leap _____?
(high)

11 _____

_____

12 _____

_____

Animal Adventure

Comparing with Adverbs In the puzzle, write the form of the adverb in parentheses that correctly completes the sentence. Then write an animal bumper sticker, using one or more comparative adverb forms.

Across

1. Lions can run ___ than zebras. (rapidly)

3. Do zebras run ___ than giraffes? (fast)

6. This deer runs ___ than that one.
   (smoothly)

9. Which of these three animals finds food
   ___? (effectively)

Down

1. Do lions sleep ___ than wolves do? (much)

2. They always arrive the ___ of all. (late)

4. Of the two, this one works ___. (well)

5. That whale swam ___ of all to us. (close)

7. Of all the seal pups, he swam the ___ of
   all. (badly)

8. This pup squealed ___ than that one.
   (little)

Bumper Sticker: _____

Name

Describe It

Do any of these topics give you any ideas?

my favorite hangout   a surprise snowstorm

a busy street   my old sneakers

the traffic officer   a special photo

the library   my homemade spaghetti

my best friend

My Description Topics List five people, places, or things that you know well enough to describe.

_____

_____

_____

_____

_____

Think about each idea you wrote. Ask yourself these questions.

Can I picture this topic clearly?

Would it make an interesting description?

Can I use at least three senses to describe it?

Would I enjoy writing about it?

Now circle the topic that you will write about.

Name

A Sense Web

Fill in the web with descriptive details about your topic. Write your topic
in the center. Then list details about it. Write words or phrases that tell
how it looks, sounds, tastes, smells, or feels to touch.

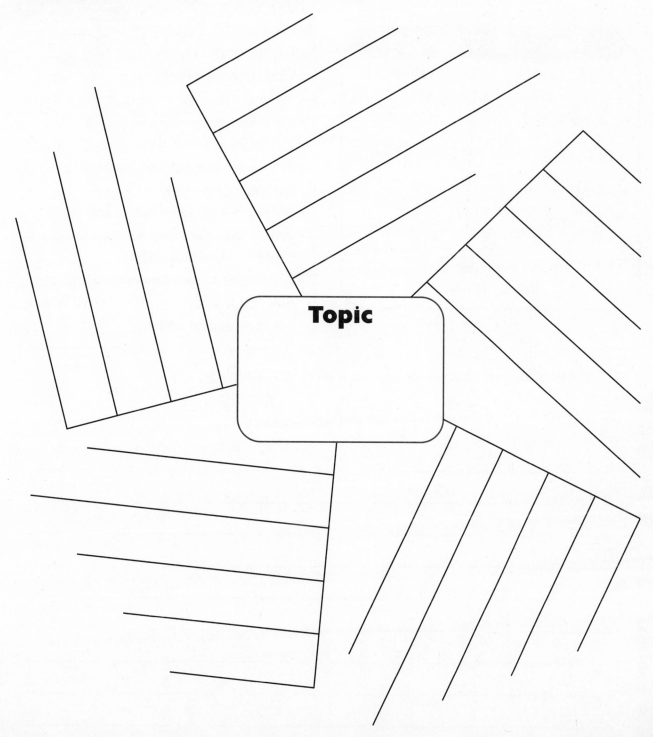

Topic

Name

Look Again

Read your description to yourself and revise it, using the Revising Checklist. Then have a writing conference with a partner. Use the Questions for a Writing Conference to help you.

• Revising Checklist •

☐ Did I describe my topic rather than tell about a personal experience?

☐ Did I include details that appeal to different senses?

☐ Did I use sense words, exact words, similes, and metaphors?

☐ Are my details organized in a way that is easy to follow?

Questions for a Writing Conference

- What do you like about this description?
- What senses are used to describe the topic? Could other senses also be used? How?
- Where are more details needed to make the description clearer?
- Do any details seem out of place?
- Which words are vague? What exact words could be used instead?
- Are similes or metaphors used? Do they describe the topic appropriately? Where could others be added?

Write notes to remember ideas from your writing conference.

My Notes

_____

_____

_____

_____

_____

_____

_____

_____

Ward Off the Word

Each vocabulary word can be used to describe either disease or pollution. Use your knowledge of the words' meanings to complete the paragraph.

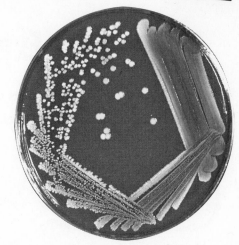

> chronic   dispersion   microbes   contaminated

The ward was restricted to people whose illnesses frequently recurred. These patients with _____ diseases had not been outside in a long time. Since the patients could catch colds easily, the room could not be _____ with exposure to _____ or any _____ of disease-causing bacteria.

Tell why each vocabulary word can be used to describe either subject— disease or pollution.

1 dispersion _____

_____

_____

2 chronic _____

_____

_____

3 contaminated _____

_____

_____

4 microbes _____

_____

_____

Name

You Are the Expert

A group of younger students wants to interview you about oil spills
and their effects. Answer their questions.

1 What is the process that describes how oil changes in a spill?

2 How do microbes affect oil in a spill?

3 Where do most oil spills occur?

4 Why do scientists know more about oil's effects on saltwater life than on freshwater life?

10 Why would oil weather slowly in Prince William Sound?

5 Why was Iraq's oil spill in 1991 so devastating?

9 How much of the coastline was coated with oil in the 1989 *Exxon Valdez* spill?

6 What species suffered the greatest threat from the Ixtoc-I spill?

8 Aside from otters and turtles, what are two other species that suffer from oil spills?

7 Why are sea otters especially affected by oil spills?

1 _____

2 _____

3 _____

4 _____

5 _____

6 _____

7 _____

8 _____

9 _____

10 _____

Name ....

Can't Complain About Canine

Label each sentence with the propaganda technique it uses: bandwagon, emotional words, overgeneralization, transfer, or testimonial.

1 Last week one fussy, annoying reader wrote in to complain that the

owners of the Canine Dog Food Factory were dumping their garbage into

our ocean. _____

2 Everyone in town knows that the owners of this factory would never do

any real damage to our waters. _____

3 The negligible amount of waste that the factory emptied into the ocean has

absolutely no effect on the water or animal life. _____

4 Our local congressional representative has given Canine Dog Food Factory

an excellent rating. _____

5 A quick glance at the beautiful beach will show you that our ocean is safe.

_____

Now write an editorial in response to the above statements. Use propaganda techniques to convince readers that the Canine Dog Food Factory is severely damaging the ocean.

To the Editor:

_____

_____

_____

_____

_____

_____

Signed,

_____

Help for Short Sentences

Here is a description of a beach and the cleanup operation after an oil spill. Rewrite the paragraph, adding prepositional phrases that describe the scene in more detail.

_____ a tugboat tows an oil tanker _____. A huge oil slick surrounds the tanker. Several boats _____ have pumps _____, and sailors are using them to retrieve the spilled oil _____. The beach _____ is a sticky mess, covered _____. _____ makeshift tables are set up, and volunteers are cleaning off seabirds with soap and water. _____ there is a fenced-in area with a sign saying "Otters." A few oil-soaked otters are inside, curled up _____. _____ hired workers spray foam to dissolve the oil _____. Volunteers rake away the oil and shovel the oily sand _____ and _____.

Prepositions					
across	at	beside	for	near	to
after	before	beyond	from	of	toward
along	behind	by	in	off	with
	below	during	into	on	

_____

_____

_____

_____

_____

_____

_____

_____

_____

_____

The Greasies

Look in the newspaper article to find the the word that answers each clue. Be careful! The meaning of the word in the article is different from the meaning in the clue. Circle the words and write them on the blanks.

Environmental Disaster!

There was a major oil spill today when a tanker failed to navigate rocky waters off the eastern Canadian coast. The tanker, bringing crude oil from the largest North Atlantic well to the refineries at New Brunswick, spilled thousands of barrels of oil into the cold, rough waters.

Scientists point out that a variety of things—including waves, wind, sunlight, and the kind of oil—determine how quickly oil will weather. Forecasts of heavy wave activity lead environmentalists to hope the oil will disperse in a few days.

Early reports indicate that some of the oil has begun to sink. Some oil has been contained, but company representatives fear that the rest will wash onto northern beaches, turning the sand into a black, sticky mess. If the oil moves farther north, it will threaten the seal colonies that inhabit the northern Canadian coast.

1 what a meteorologist predicts _____

2 where dishes are washed _____

3 a hand signal that means "hi" _____

4 to lie down and relax without sleeping _____

5 a high-ranking military officer _____

6 helpful and gentle _____

7 to slide down a hill on a sled _____

8 in good health; not sick _____

9 to smooth wood by rubbing with rough paper _____

10 paper sticker used to close an envelope _____

Name

After the Words Spill

Use the clues to complete the sentences. The shaded boxes contain a hidden word.

contaminated	grooming	chronic	petroleum	plankton
dispersion	microbes	pollutants	weathering	reef
hydrocarbons	crude	sublethal	sediment	

1 Bacteria or fungi that help to break down oil are ___ ___ ___ ___ ___ ___ ___ ___.

2 Sea otters do this with their fur. ___ ___ ___ ___ ___ ___ ___ ___

3 The oil ___ ___ ___ ___ ___ ___ ___ ___ ___ ___ ___ ___ the shoreline with dangerous chemicals.

4 When this occurs, everything scatters. ___ ___ ___ ___ ___ ___ ___ ___ ___ ___

5 Coral is found on a ___ ___ ___ ___.

6 The process of breaking down oil is ___ ___ ___ ___ ___ ___ ___ ___ ___ ___.

7 Lightweight compounds within oil are

___ ___ ___ ___ ___ ___ ___ ___ ___ ___ ___ ___.

8 It depends on the nutrients found over the continental shelves.

___ ___ ___ ___ ___ ___ ___ ___

9 Raw or unrefined ___ ___ ___ ___ ___ oil can harm oceans.

10 When an effect of an oil spill is invisible but permanent, it is

___ ___ ___ ___ ___ ___ ___ ___ ___.

11 Another name for oil is ___ ___ ___ ___ ___ ___ ___ ___ ___.

12 If this is made out of clay, oil sticking to it will not break down as fast.

___ ___ ___ ___ ___ ___ ___ ___

13 Things that cause pollution are ___ ___ ___ ___ ___ ___ ___ ___ ___ ___.

14 A ___ ___ ___ ___ ___ ___ ___ infection will last a long time.

What is the hidden word?

Name

Sea Otter Rescue

The Prefix *ob-* Each Spelling Word has the prefix *ob-*, meaning "against," "toward," or "down." The prefix *ob-* can also be spelled *oc-* or *op-* to match the first letter of the following base word or word root.

ob + serve = observe
ob + cur   = occur
ob + pose   = oppose

Help rescue the sea otters from the oil slick. Draw a line from each otter to the correct form of the prefix *ob-* to form a Spelling Word. Then write each word below the matching prefix.

Spelling Words

1. occur
2. observe
3. obtain
4. oppose
5. object
6. obstruct
7. occupy
8. obvious
9. occasion
10. oppress

My Study List
What other words do you need to study for spelling? Add them to My Study List for *After the Spill* in the back of this book.

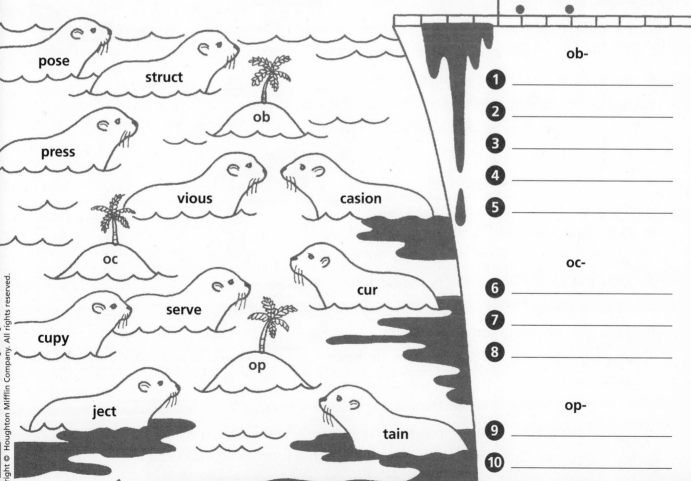

pose

struct

ob

press

vious

casion

oc

serve

cur

cupy

op

ject

tain

ob-

1 _____
2 _____
3 _____
4 _____
5 _____

oc-

6 _____
7 _____
8 _____

op-

9 _____
10 _____

Name

Spelling Spree

Proofreading
Find and circle four misspelled Spelling Words in this television news report. Then write each word correctly.

A protest is expected to ocurr at the SLICK Oil Company today. The protesters oppose SLICK's use of an aging fleet of rusted oil tankers, claiming they pose an obveous threat to the environment. Protesters hope to obtane permission from City Hall to stage the protest on the pier where the tankers are docked. Our reporters will be there to opserve the event, broadcasting to you live with all the action!

Spelling Words

1. occur
2. observe
3. obtain
4. oppose
5. object
6. obstruct
7. occupy
8. obvious
9. occasion
10. oppress

1 _____

2 _____

3 _____

4 _____

Word Changes
Follow the directions to change one Spelling Word into another. Write the words.

5. Write the word that is a synonym for *block.*

6. Replace the four middle letters with two others to write the word that means "express a different view."

7. Write the word that means "an important event."

8. Then replace the last five letters with three others to write the word that means "inhabit."

9. Write the word that means "to burden by abuse of power."

10. Replace the last four letters with three others to write the word that means "to be or fight against."

5 _____

6 _____

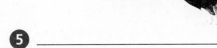

7 _____

8 _____

9 _____

10 _____

Meet the Press
Imagine that you are a spokesperson for an oil company. One of your company's tankers has just run aground and is leaking oil. On a separate sheet of paper, write a statement to read at a press conference about this accident. Use Spelling Words from the list.

Seabeach Times

Prepositional Phrases as Adjectives
Underline the prepositional phrase in each sentence and write the preposition.

preposition	object		preposition	object
Oil **from** the spill covered the rocks **on** the beach.
prepositional phrase · prepositional phrase

Seabeach Times

Volunteers Rescue Sea Life

Yesterday's oil spill was a disaster for our seashore. All the sea life around our area is severely threatened.

Volunteers from Seabeach have been working day and night. Their concern for the animals is overwhelming. Hundreds of people were needed, and hundreds have come. What do they do? Animals under the oil are recovered, rocks on the shore are scrubbed, birds along the beach are cleaned, and everything beside the oily waters is examined. The volunteers do anything of use.

A rescue center in the school gym houses otters. Another center by the local college has become a nursery for baby animals. The church across town has established a rest area behind the building. Communities from Seabeach to Soundview are all working hard, and cooperation during this difficult time is high.

1 _____
2 _____
3 _____
4 _____
5 _____
6 _____
7 _____
8 _____
9 _____
10 _____
11 _____
12 _____
13 _____
14 _____
15 _____
16 _____
17 _____
18 _____

Tanker Trouble

Prepositional Phrases as Adjectives

Color the oil drums that contain prepositional
phrases. Then use the prepositional phrases
to complete the sentences. Underline the
noun or pronoun each phrase modifies.
Finally, write three sentences, using words from the
other drums and the prepositional phrases as adjectives.

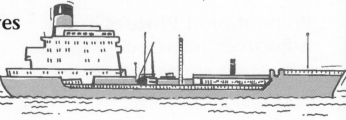

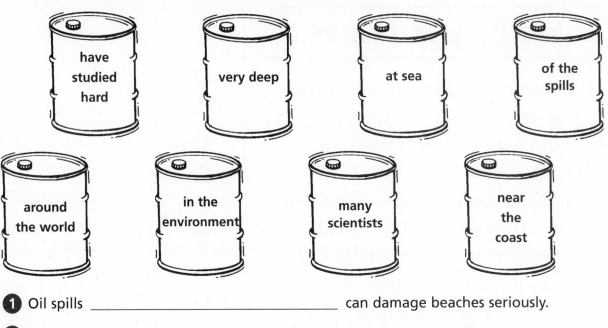

have
studied
hard

very deep

at sea

of the
spills

around
the world

in the
environment

many
scientists

near
the
coast

1 Oil spills _____ can damage beaches seriously.

2 Those _____ threaten deep-sea life.

3 Many factors _____ can affect the damage.

4 Scientists carefully study photographs _____.

5 Marine biologists _____ monitor the spill areas.

6 _____

_____

7 _____

_____

8 _____

Name ....

Company PR

You are the head of public relations at a large paper company. Recently, people have claimed that your factory is polluting a nearby beach. Complete this memo to inform employees about the problem and your plans for action. Use words from the box and words and phrases of your own.

targeted	boycotting	protested	image
presentation	campaign	public relations	

TO: All Royal Paper Employees

FROM: _____, Director of Public Relations

     Several recent news stories claim that the Royal Paper Factory is polluting Crystal Beach. People who live near Crystal Beach have _____ this pollution by picketing the factory. They are also _____ Royal Paper products, so we can expect company sales to _____. Unfortunately, the protesters have also _____ some Royal Paper officials by _____. Needless to say, our company's fine _____ has suffered, and many people now see Royal Paper as _____.

    As head of _____ for Royal, it is my job to _____. Therefore, I have scheduled a _____ at which the protesters will meet with company officials so that we can all _____. We also plan to begin a new advertising _____ that will make Royal Paper _____. Our new slogan is:

_____.

Name _____

Plan of Action

Complete this chart to show how Joel solved the dolphins' dilemma.

Problem

Solution

Four steps toward the solution

Outcome

Name ....

Well, In My Opinion . . .

Read each editorial and write what you think the writer's bias is. Underline any emotional words or assumptions that you see in the passage.

What's wrong with these kids today? If you ask me, they've all gone nuts over the environment. There were mobs of them out crying over a few dolphins that got caught in our nets. Their friends all jumped on the bandwagon, and pretty soon they blackmailed the tuna companies into slapping a ban on us. Now dozens of honest tuna fishers are out of work. Of course, nobody's crying over that!

Author's bias: _____

_____

_____

_____

_____

River Woods, one of Cedarton's last jewels, is about to be blasted off the face of the earth. That's right, the greedy real-estate developers are already plotting to foist another ugly mall on our community. Fine old oak trees, songbirds, and fresh air—our natural heritage—will be replaced by more concrete, congestion, and crime. It's enough to make you sick!

Author's bias: _____

_____

_____

_____

_____

Write a paragraph supporting the opening of an oil refinery in your town.
Use assumptions and emotional words to emphasize your point.

_____

_____

_____

_____

_____

_____

_____

Dolphin Dilemma

You ordered 200 dolphin pins from the Pick-a-Pin Company for a fund-raising project. When your order arrived, there were only 198 pins, and 19 were broken. You paid $5 for each pin when you placed your order.

Write a letter to Customer Service at the Pick-a-Pin Company (1234 Main St., Suite 15, Los Angeles, CA 90086) to report your problem. Decide what you want the company to do about it. Use this page to plan your letter. Then write the letter on another sheet of paper.

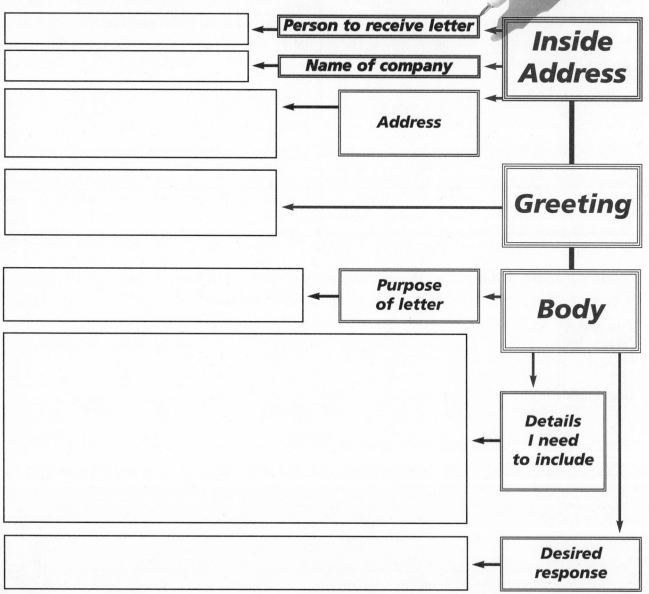

Person to receive letter

Name of company

Address

Inside Address

Greeting

Purpose of letter

Body

Details I need to include

Desired response

Joel Rubin

Pigeon Plight

A classroom of sixth graders sent this letter to their mayor. Circle words containing noun suffixes *-ation*, *-ment*, *-ion*, or *-ness*, and verb suffixes *-ize*, *-ify*, or *-en*. Use them to complete the chart below.

October 5, 1996

Dear Mayor Jones,

There must be some confusion! You have shown very poor judgment! Did you really authorize the sanitation bureau to terrorize the poor pigeons that nest in the town hall without giving the local humane society proper notification? The town hall is public property. There is no regulation saying birds can't nest there, but you went ahead and ordered their extermination for doing so.

You claim you want to beautify the town hall, and that the birds are responsible for its dirtiness. You must realize that there are other ways of keeping things clean that wouldn't harm the pigeons. Please don't harden your heart to their problem.

Sincerely,

Mrs. Bing's sixth grade class

	Word	Base Word	Suffix	Part of Speech
1				
2				
3				
4				
5				
6				
7				
8				
9				
10				
11				
12				

Cross Words

Use the clues to fill in the puzzle. All words appear in the selection.

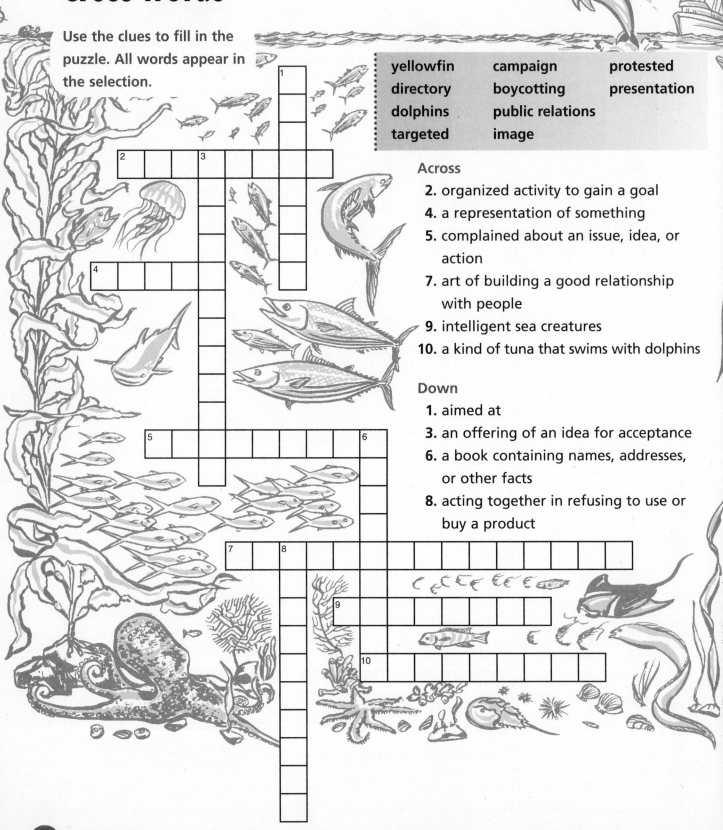

yellowfin	campaign	protested
directory	boycotting	presentation
dolphins	public relations	
targeted	image	

Across

2. organized activity to gain a goal
4. a representation of something
5. complained about an issue, idea, or action
7. art of building a good relationship with people
9. intelligent sea creatures
10. a kind of tuna that swims with dolphins

Down

1. aimed at
3. an offering of an idea for acceptance
6. a book containing names, addresses, or other facts
8. acting together in refusing to use or buy a product

Name

Victory at Sea

The Prefix *ad-* Each Spelling Word begins with the prefix *ad-* meaning "to" or "toward." The spelling of the prefix *ad-* often changes to match the first letter of the following base word or word root.

ad + vice = advice   ad + peal = appeal
ad + cuse = accuse   ad + sume = assume
ad + rive = arrive

Help the dolphin escape the drift net. Write the correct spelling of the prefix *ad-* to complete each Spelling Word on the dolphin. Then write each word on the tuna can with the matching prefix.

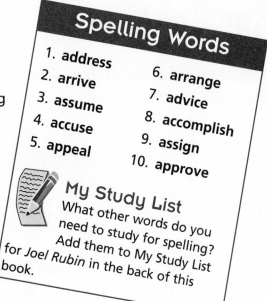

Spelling Words

1. address
2. arrive
3. assume
4. accuse
5. appeal
6. arrange
7. advice
8. accomplish
9. assign
10. approve

My Study List
What other words do you need to study for spelling? Add them to My Study List for *Joel Rubin* in the back of this book.

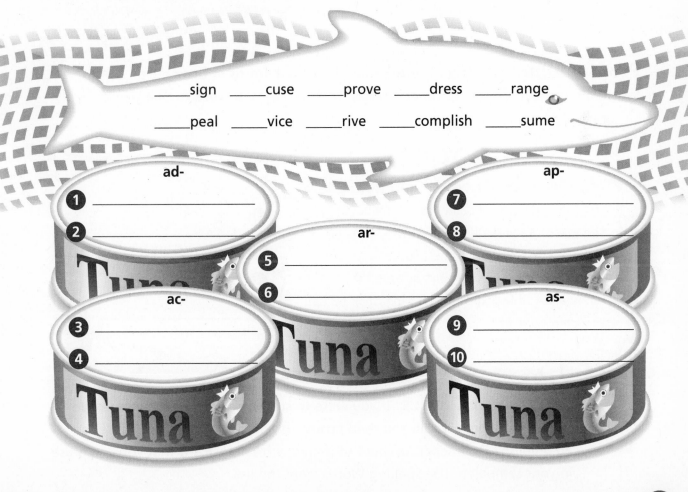

_____sign   _____cuse   _____prove   _____dress   _____range

_____peal   _____vice   _____rive   _____complish   _____sume

ad-
1 _____
2 _____

ar-
5 _____
6 _____

ap-
7 _____
8 _____

ac-
3 _____
4 _____

as-
9 _____
10 _____

Name ....

Spelling Spree

Crossword Puzzle Write the
Spelling Word that fits each clue.

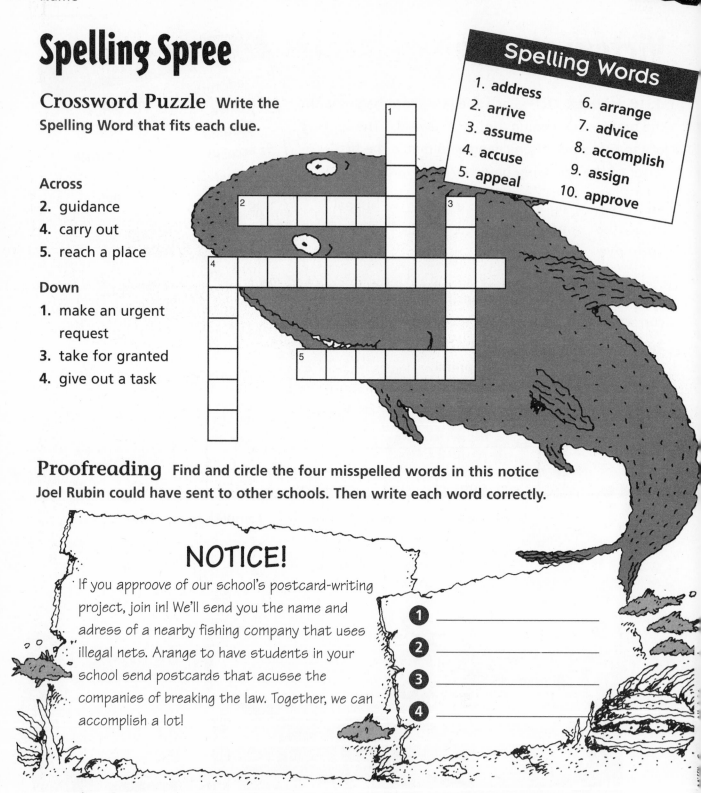

Spelling Words

1. address
2. arrive
3. assume
4. accuse
5. appeal
6. arrange
7. advice
8. accomplish
9. assign
10. approve

Across

2. guidance

4. carry out

5. reach a place

Down

1. make an urgent request

3. take for granted

4. give out a task

Proofreading Find and circle the four misspelled words in this notice
Joel Rubin could have sent to other schools. Then write each word correctly.

NOTICE!

If you approove of our school's postcard-writing project, join in! We'll send you the name and adress of a nearby fishing company that uses illegal nets. Arange to have students in your school send postcards that acusse the companies of breaking the law. Together, we can accomplish a lot!

1. _____
2. _____
3. _____
4. _____

Campaign Tactics If you were to start a postcard campaign like Joel Rubin's, to whom would you send postcards and what would you hope to accomplish? On a separate sheet of paper, write a postcard that you could use in your campaign. Use Spelling Words from the list.

Dolphin Details

Name

Modifies Verb

Dolphins swim in all the oceans.

Modifies Adjective

Dolphins are friendly toward people.

Modifies Adverb

Dolphins leap high above the water.

Prepositional Phrases as Adverbs Here are some sentences from an encyclopedia article about dolphins. Underline each prepositional phrase used as an adverb. Write the word or words that each phrase modifies. Then write a sentence of your own. Use at least one prepositional phrase as an adverb.

1 Dolphins always seem ready for adventure. _____

2 They live almost everywhere in the world's oceans. _____

3 Dolphins swim with their tail flukes. _____

4 Sometimes dolphins are visible under the water. _____

5 They can dive deep below the surface. _____

6 A dolphin navigates by sound. _____

7 Through its melon, the dolphin broadcasts a sound. _____

8 The sound hits an object somewhere near the dolphin. _____

9 After a time, the sound returns to the dolphin. _____

10 In the water, the dolphin is balanced by its dorsal fin and flipper. _____

11 _____

_____

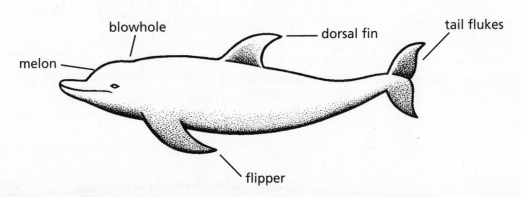

blowhole

dorsal fin

tail flukes

melon

flipper

Joel Rubin

Cruise in Good Company

Prepositional Phrases as Adverbs A cruise company sponsors daily trips to watch dolphins in the ocean. Help prepare a brochure to advertise the cruises. Write a sentence or two for each picture below. Use at least one adverb phrase in each sentence.

1 _____

2 _____

3 _____

4 _____

5 _____

6 _____

Name _____

I Must Protest!

Write a letter to protest and change a problem you read about in Ocean Quest. Complete this page to help you plan your letter.

What problem do you want to change?	
What difference would this change make for the future?	
To whom will you write? It could be one person, a group, or a company.	
What views or assumptions do you think the person(s) you are addressing will make about the problem? What assumptions do you make? Compare the two points of view.	**Their views:** **My views:**
What actions should be taken to solve the problem?	

Checklist

Use your notes to write a first draft of your letter. Before you write your final draft, check your letter against this list:

- ❏ My letter shows the importance of the ocean for our future.

- ❏ My letter explains my views clearly.

- ❏ My letter compares my views with those of the person(s) I am addressing.

- ❏ My letter lists possible solutions to the problem.

STUDENT HANDBOOK

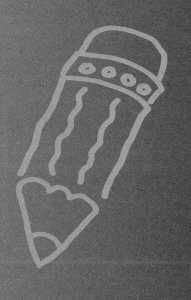

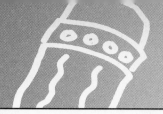

Contents

INDEPENDENT READING LOG

Use this log to record the books or other materials you read on your own.

Date ______________________________

Author ______________________________

Title ______________________________

Notes and Comments ______________________________

____

____

____

____

Date ______________________________

Author ______________________________

Title ______________________________

Notes and Comments ______________________________

____

____

____

____

Date _____

Author _____

Title _____

Notes and Comments _____

_____

_____

_____

_____

Date _____

Author _____

Title _____

Notes and Comments _____

_____

_____

_____

_____

Date _____

Author _____

Title _____

Notes and Comments _____

_____

_____

_____

_____

Date _____

Author _____

Title _____

Notes and Comments _____

_____

_____

_____

_____

Date _____

Author _____

Title _____

Notes and Comments _____

_____

_____

_____

_____

Date _____

Author _____

Title _____

Notes and Comments _____

_____

_____

_____

_____

Date _____

Author _____

Title _____

Notes and Comments _____

_____

_____

_____

_____

Date _____

Author _____

Title _____

Notes and Comments _____

_____

_____

_____

_____

Date _____

Author _____

Title _____

Notes and Comments _____

_____

_____

_____

_____

How to Study a Word

1 **LOOK** at the word.
- What letters are in the word?
- What does the word mean? Does it have more than one meaning?

2 **SAY** the word.
- What are the consonant sounds?
- What are the vowel sounds?

3 **THINK** about the word.
- How is each sound spelled?
- Did you see any familiar spelling patterns?
- Did you note any prefixes, suffixes, or other word parts?

4 **WRITE** the word.
- Think about the sounds and the letters.
- Form the letters correctly.

5 **CHECK** the spelling.
- Did you spell the word the same way it is spelled in your word list?
- Do you need to write the word again in your notebook?

accept	busy	fourth	nickel	to
ache	buy	Friday	ninety	too
again	by	friend	ninety-nine	tried
all right	calendar	goes	ninth	tries
almost	cannot	going	often	truly
already	can't	grammar	once	two
although	careful	guard	other	tying
always	catch	guess	people	unknown
angel	caught	guide	principal	until
angle	chief	half	quiet	unusual
answer	children	haven't	quit	wasn't
argue	choose	hear	quite	wear
asked	chose	heard	really	weather
aunt	color	heavy	receive	Wednesday
author	cough	height	rhythm	weird
awful	cousin	here	right	we'll
babies	decide	hers	Saturday	we're
been	divide	hole	stretch	weren't
believe	does	hoping	surely	we've
bother	don't	hour	their	where
bought	early	its	theirs	which
break	enough	it's	there	whole
breakfast	every	January	they're	witch
breathe	exact	let's	they've	won't
broken	except	listen	those	wouldn't
brother	excite	loose	though	write
brought	expect	lose	thought	writing
bruise	February	minute	through	written
build	finally	muscle	tied	you're
business	forty	neighbor	tired	yours

Island of the Blue Dolphins

Final Schwa + *n* or *l*

| lən | ➔ | weap**on**, hidd**en** |
| ləl | ➔ | trem**ble**, jew**el**, usu**al** |

Spelling Words

1. tremble
2. battle
3. weapon
4. usual
5. reason
6. jewel
7. hidden
8. several
9. lessen
10. tunnel

Challenge Words

1. coral
2. companion
3. omen
4. horizon
5. gradual

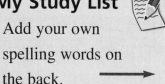

My Study List

Add your own spelling words on the back. ➔

Tonweya and the Eagles

Final Schwa + *r*

| lər | ➔ | dang**er**, terr**or**, li**ar** |

Spelling Words

1. danger
2. feather
3. shiver
4. terror
5. hunger
6. shoulder
7. quarter
8. error
9. liar
10. popular

Challenge Words

1. warrior
2. survivor
3. similar
4. character
5. calendar

My Study List

Add your own spelling words on the back. ➔

Bearstone

Words with *ie* or *ei*

ie	➔	p**ie**ce
after c ➔ ei	➔	rec**ei**ve
lāl ➔ ei	➔	**ei**ght

Spelling Words

1. piece
2. eight
3. believe
4. weight
5. reins
6. brief
7. relieve
8. sleigh
9. receive
10. ceiling

Challenge Words

1. retrieve
2. deceit
3. wield
4. achievement
5. beige

My Study List

Add your own spelling words on the back. ➔

Spelling and Writing Word Lists

Name _____

 My Study List

1. _____
2. _____
3. _____
4. _____
5. _____
6. _____
7. _____
8. _____
9. _____
10. _____

Selection Vocabulary

You may want to use these words in your own writing.

1. trailhead
2. claustrophobic
3. wilderness
4. canyon
5. rapids
6. veered

How to Study a Word

LOOK at the word.
SAY the word.
THINK about the word.
WRITE the word.
CHECK the spelling.

298

Spelling and Writing Word Lists

Name _____

 My Study List

1. _____
2. _____
3. _____
4. _____
5. _____
6. _____
7. _____
8. _____
9. _____
10. _____

Selection Vocabulary

You may want to use these words in your own writing.

1. sacred
2. sheer
3. defiantly
4. cleft
5. ravenously

How to Study a Word

LOOK at the word.
SAY the word.
THINK about the word.
WRITE the word.
CHECK the spelling.

298

Spelling and Writing Word Lists

Name _____

 My Study List

1. _____
2. _____
3. _____
4. _____
5. _____
6. _____
7. _____
8. _____
9. _____
10. _____

Selection Vocabulary

You may want to use these words in your own writing.

1. drifted
2. slinking
3. skirted
4. seeping
5. chafing

How to Study a Word

LOOK at the word.
SAY the word.
THINK about the word.
WRITE the word.
CHECK the spelling.

298

Last Summer with Maizon

The VCCV and VCCCV Patterns

VC|CV	→	ab|sent
VCC|V	→	snick|er
V|CCV	→	tro|phy
VC|CCV	→	in|stead
VCC|CV	→	emp|ty

Spelling Words

1. empty
2. absent
3. whisper
4. laughter
5. instead
6. surround
7. applaud
8. trophy
9. swallow
10. snicker

Challenge Words

1. frantic
2. beckon
3. offend
4. somber
5. technique

My Study List

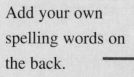

Add your own spelling words on the back. →

The No-Guitar Blues

Compound Words

A **compound word** may be written as one word, as a hyphenated word, or as separate words.

Spelling Words

1. teenager
2. freeway
3. secondhand
4. living room
5. wrongdoing
6. wallpaper
7. dog tag
8. warehouse
9. old-fashioned
10. brother-in-law

Challenge Words

1. junior high school
2. disk jockey
3. self-conscious
4. software
5. extraordinary

My Study List

Add your own spelling words on the back. →

Maniac Magee

Homophones

Homophones are words that sound alike but have different spellings and meanings.

Spelling Words

1. threw
2. through
3. hall
4. haul
5. stare
6. stair
7. heard
8. herd
9. waste
10. waist

Challenge Words

1. faint
2. feint
3. idle
4. idol
5. idyll

My Study List

Add your own spelling words on the back. →

Name _____

 My Study List

1. _____
2. _____
3. _____
4. _____
5. _____
6. _____
7. _____
8. _____
9. _____
10. _____

Selection Vocabulary

You may want to use these words in your own writing.

1. boundary
2. instincts
3. fatal
4. prospects

How to Study a Word

LOOK at the word.
SAY the word.
THINK about the word.
WRITE the word.
CHECK the spelling.

300

Name _____

 My Study List

1. _____
2. _____
3. _____
4. _____
5. _____
6. _____
7. _____
8. _____
9. _____
10. _____

Selection Vocabulary

You may want to use these words in your own writing.

1. deceitful
2. privacy
3. mimicked
4. wrongdoing
5. confident

How to Study a Word

LOOK at the word.
SAY the word.
THINK about the word.
WRITE the word.
CHECK the spelling.

300

Name _____

 My Study List

1. _____
2. _____
3. _____
4. _____
5. _____
6. _____
7. _____
8. _____
9. _____
10. _____

Selection Vocabulary

You may want to use these words in your own writing.

1. desolate
2. distracted
3. relieve
4. somberly

How to Study a Word

LOOK at the word.
SAY the word.
THINK about the word.
WRITE the word.
CHECK the spelling.

300

Into the Mummy's Tomb

Adding *-ed* or *-ing*

wrap + **ed** = wrap**ped**

slip + **ing** = slip**ping**

begin + **ing** = begin**ning**

<u>cov</u>er + **ed** = cov**ered**

Spelling Words

1. wrapped
2. beginning
3. covered
4. happened
5. slipping
6. suffered
7. setting
8. entered
9. forgetting
10. preferred

Challenge Words

1. flattened
2. murdered
3. tarred
4. strengthened
5. equipped

My Study List

Add your own spelling words on the back. →

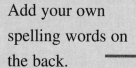

301

The Star Fisher

Spelling the |sh| Sound

|sh| → a**sh**amed, emo**ti**on, so**ci**al, ti**ss**ue

Spelling Words

1. ashamed
2. social
3. especially
4. emotion
5. partial
6. solution
7. fashion
8. sheriff
9. tissue
10. session

Challenge Words

1. auction
2. famished
3. humiliation
4. politician
5. ferocious

My Study List

Add your own spelling words on the back. →

301

The Scholarship Jacket

The VCV Pattern

VC|V → min|ute

V|CV → a|ward
        ea|ger

Spelling Words

1. award
2. eager
3. refuse
4. minute
5. avoid
6. labor
7. fever
8. body
9. promise
10. panic

Challenge Words

1. scholar
2. resign
3. agile
4. solemn
5. motive

My Study List

Add your own spelling words on the back. →

301

Name _____

 My Study List

1. _____
2. _____
3. _____
4. _____
5. _____
6. _____
7. _____
8. _____
9. _____
10. _____

Selection Vocabulary

You may want to use these words in your own writing.

1. tradition
2. despaired
3. resign
4. dismay
5. dignity
6. significance

How to Study a Word

LOOK at the word.
SAY the word.
THINK about the word.
WRITE the word.
CHECK the spelling.

Name _____

 My Study List

1. _____
2. _____
3. _____
4. _____
5. _____
6. _____
7. _____
8. _____
9. _____
10. _____

Selection Vocabulary

You may want to use these words in your own writing.

1. humiliated
2. etiquette
3. ridicule
4. cringed

How to Study a Word

LOOK at the word.
SAY the word.
THINK about the word.
WRITE the word.
CHECK the spelling.

Name _____

 My Study List

1. _____
2. _____
3. _____
4. _____
5. _____
6. _____
7. _____
8. _____
9. _____
10. _____

Selection Vocabulary

You may want to use these words in your own writing.

1. tomb
2. archaeologist
3. artifacts
4. sarcophagus
5. shroud
6. pharaoh
7. mummy

How to Study a Word

LOOK at the word.
SAY the word.
THINK about the word.
WRITE the word.
CHECK the spelling.

The Iceman

More Words with -ion

deci**de**	➡	deci**sion**
inten**d**	➡	inten**tion**

Spelling Words

1. decide
2. decision
3. conclude
4. conclusion
5. attend
6. attention
7. erode
8. erosion
9. intend
10. intention

Challenge Words

1. provide
2. provision
3. corrode
4. corrosion

My Study List

Add your own spelling words on the back. ➡

Dig This! How Archaeologists Uncover Our Past

Adding -ion or -ation

construct	➡	construc**tion**
inform	➡	inform**ation**
locate	➡	loca**tion**
explore	➡	explor**ation**

Spelling Words

1. locate
2. location
3. inform
4. information
5. construct
6. construction
7. explore
8. exploration
9. examine
10. examination

Challenge Words

1. excavate
2. excavation
3. determine
4. determination

My Study List

Add your own spelling words on the back. ➡

Tales Mummies Tell

Adding Endings and Suffixes

prov**e**	+	**ed**	=	prov**ed**
hand**le**	+	**ed**	=	hand**led**
lik**e**	+	**ly**	=	lik**ely**

Spelling Words

1. likely
2. proved
3. loosest
4. serving
5. closeness
6. simply
7. placement
8. shapeless
9. gently
10. handled

Challenge Words

1. probably
2. fractured
3. precisely
4. indicated
5. irritating

My Study List

Add your own spelling words on the back. ➡

Name_____

 My Study List

1. _____
2. _____
3. _____
4. _____
5. _____
6. _____
7. _____
8. _____
9. _____
10. _____

Selection Vocabulary

You may want to use these words in your own writing.

1. autopsies
2. techniques
3. embalmers
4. amputated
5. preserved
6. evidence
7. corpse

How to Study a Word

LOOK at the word.
SAY the word.
THINK about the word.
WRITE the word.
CHECK the spelling.

Spelling and Writing Word Lists

Name_____

 My Study List

1. _____
2. _____
3. _____
4. _____
5. _____
6. _____
7. _____
8. _____
9. _____
10. _____

Selection Vocabulary

You may want to use these words in your own writing.

1. prehistoric
2. decomposed
3. site
4. cultures
5. ruins

How to Study a Word

LOOK at the word.
SAY the word.
THINK about the word.
WRITE the word.
CHECK the spelling.

304

Spelling and Writing Word Lists

Name_____

 My Study List

1. _____
2. _____
3. _____
4. _____
5. _____
6. _____
7. _____
8. _____
9. _____
10. _____

Selection Vocabulary

You may want to use these words in your own writing.

1. amateurs
2. primitive
3. estimate
4. glaciers
5. exposure

How to Study a Word

LOOK at the word.
SAY the word.
THINK about the word.
WRITE the word.
CHECK the spelling.

304

The Moon and I

The Prefixes *dis-*, *mis-*, and *ex-*

dis- ➔ **dis**continue

mis- ➔ **mis**understand

ex- ➔ **ex**pect

Spelling Words

1. example
2. discontinue
3. expect
4. experience
5. distance
6. dissolve
7. disease
8. misspell
9. misunderstand
10. mischief

Challenge Words

1. dissatisfied
2. exaggerate
3. misinterpret
4. disadvantage
5. mispronounce

My Study List

Add your own spelling words on the back. ➔

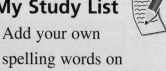

Faith Ringgold

Plurals of Words Ending with *o*

stud**io** ➔ stud**ios**

sol**o** ➔ sol**os**

her**o** ➔ her**oes**

Spelling Words

1. heroes
2. studios
3. radios
4. potatoes
5. mottoes
6. solos
7. pianos
8. echoes
9. stereos
10. volcanoes

Challenge Words

1. mementos
2. tuxedos
3. ghettos
4. avocados
5. vetoes

My Study List

Add your own spelling words on the back. ➔

The Phantom Tollbooth

Plurals of Words Ending with *f*

roo**f** ➔ roo**fs**

lea**f** ➔ lea**ves**

pu**ff** ➔ pu**ffs**

li**fe** ➔ li**ves**

Spelling Words

1. leaves
2. puffs
3. roofs
4. loaves
5. lives
6. beliefs
7. halves
8. shelves
9. thieves
10. chiefs

Challenge Words

1. themselves
2. tariffs
3. kerchiefs
4. wharves
5. chefs

My Study List

Add your own spelling words on the back. ➔

My Study List

1. _____
2. _____
3. _____
4. _____
5. _____
6. _____
7. _____
8. _____
9. _____
10. _____

Selection Vocabulary

You may want to use these words in your own writing.

1. dejectedly
2. wistfully
3. expectations
4. procrastinating

How to Study a Word

LOOK at the word.
SAY the word.
THINK about the word.
WRITE the word.
CHECK the spelling.

 My Study List

1. _____
2. _____
3. _____
4. _____
5. _____
6. _____
7. _____
8. _____
9. _____
10. _____

Selection Vocabulary

You may want to use these words in your own writing.

1. heritage
2. dimension
3. medium
4. abstract
5. convey
6. composition
7. legacy

How to Study a Word

LOOK at the word.
SAY the word.
THINK about the word.
WRITE the word.
CHECK the spelling.

 My Study List

1. _____
2. _____
3. _____
4. _____
5. _____
6. _____
7. _____
8. _____
9. _____
10. _____

Selection Vocabulary

You may want to use these words in your own writing.

1. resort
2. patiently
3. revisions
4. desperate
5. manuscripts
6. unexpectedly

How to Study a Word

LOOK at the word.
SAY the word.
THINK about the word.
WRITE the word.
CHECK the spelling.

The Wrong Lunch Line

Words That End with -ant or -ent

|əntl| ➔ pleas**ant**, diff**erent**

Spelling Words

1. different
2. pleasant
3. ignorant
4. patient
5. moment
6. frequent
7. important
8. student
9. vacant
10. brilliant

Challenge Words

1. incident
2. persistent
3. tolerant
4. innocent
5. participant

My Study List

Add your own spelling words on the back. ➔

Pacific Crossing

Words That End with -ize or -ise

|īz| ➔ real**ize**, exerc**ise**

Spelling Words

1. exercise
2. realize
3. finalize
4. surprise
5. recognize
6. criticize
7. specialize
8. memorize
9. advertise
10. organize

Challenge Words

1. formalize
2. computerize
3. commercialize
4. customize
5. symbolize

My Study List

Add your own spelling words on the back. ➔

The Wright Brothers

The Prefixes per-, pre, and pro-

per- ➔ perform
pre- ➔ prepare
pro- ➔ process

Spelling Words

1. prepare
2. process
3. perform
4. problem
5. perfect
6. propose
7. persist
8. preview
9. profession
10. prehistoric

Challenge Words

1. propel
2. precaution
3. perception
4. prosecute
5. persecute

My Study List

Add your own spelling words on the back. ➔

Spelling and Writing Word Lists

Spelling and Writing Word Lists

Spelling and Writing Word Lists

Name _____

 My Study List

1. _____
2. _____
3. _____
4. _____
5. _____
6. _____
7. _____
8. _____
9. _____
10. _____

Selection Vocabulary

You may want to use these words in your own writing.

1. calculations
2. data
3. absorbed
4. systematic
5. tedious
6. accuracy
7. stabilize

How to Study a Word

LOOK at the word.
SAY the word.
THINK about the word.
WRITE the word.
CHECK the spelling.

308

Name _____

 My Study List

1. _____
2. _____
3. _____
4. _____
5. _____
6. _____
7. _____
8. _____
9. _____
10. _____

Selection Vocabulary

You may want to use these words in your own writing.

1. tournament
2. dedicated
3. meditation
4. practitioners
5. executed

How to Study a Word

LOOK at the word.
SAY the word.
THINK about the word.
WRITE the word.
CHECK the spelling.

308

Name _____

 My Study List

1. _____
2. _____
3. _____
4. _____
5. _____
6. _____
7. _____
8. _____
9. _____
10. _____

Selection Vocabulary

You may want to use these words in your own writing.

1. anxiously
2. reassurance
3. persisted
4. suppressed
5. nonchalantly
6. impulsively

How to Study a Word

LOOK at the word.
SAY the word.
THINK about the word.
WRITE the word.
CHECK the spelling.

308

Oceans

Take-Home Word Lists

The Pinballs

Take-Home Word Lists

Shiloh

The Prefix *in-*

in- → in-, im-
include,
immense,
import

Spelling Words

1. immense
2. include
3. import
4. involve
5. impossible
6. immediate
7. inquire
8. incomplete
9. immigrant
10. individual

Challenge Words

1. inspiration
2. imply
3. infer
4. inadequate
5. infinite

Words That End with *-able* or *-ible*

-able → lov**able**
-ible → incred**ible**

Spelling Words

1. lovable
2. possible
3. probable
4. believable
5. reasonable
6. breakable
7. terrible
8. responsible
9. incredible
10. visible

Challenge Words

1. admirable
2. sociable
3. imaginable
4. favorable
5. edible

Words That End with *-ance* or *-ence*

|ənsl or → allow**ance**
|nsl → sil**ence**

Spelling Words

1. silence
2. difference
3. allowance
4. violence
5. importance
6. appearance
7. entrance
8. sentence
9. audience
10. performance

Challenge Words

1. persistence
2. innocence
3. resemblance
4. magnificence
5. deliverance

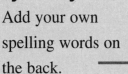

My Study List

Add your own
spelling words on
the back. →

My Study List

Add your own
spelling words on
the back. →

My Study List

Add your own
spelling words on
the back. →

Name _____

My Study List

1. _____
2. _____
3. _____
4. _____
5. _____
6. _____
7. _____
8. _____
9. _____
10. _____

Selection Vocabulary

You may want to use these words in your own writing.

1. suspicions
2. mistreat
3. obliged

How to Study a Word

LOOK at the word.
SAY the word.
THINK about the word.
WRITE the word.
CHECK the spelling.

Name _____

My Study List

1. _____
2. _____
3. _____
4. _____
5. _____
6. _____
7. _____
8. _____
9. _____
10. _____

Selection Vocabulary

You may want to use these words in your own writing.

1. claimed
2. distrusted
3. hesitated

How to Study a Word

LOOK at the word.
SAY the word.
THINK about the word.
WRITE the word.
CHECK the spelling.

Name _____

My Study List

1. _____
2. _____
3. _____
4. _____
5. _____
6. _____
7. _____
8. _____
9. _____
10. _____

Selection Vocabulary

You may want to use these words in your own writing.

1. evaporates
2. condenses
3. currents
4. moderates
5. gravitational
6. rotates

How to Study a Word

LOOK at the word.
SAY the word.
THINK about the word.
WRITE the word.
CHECK the spelling.

Joel Rubin

The Prefix *ad-*

ad- ➔ ad-, ac-, ar-, as-

advice
accuse
arrive
assume

Spelling Words

1. address
2. arrive
3. assume
4. accuse
5. appeal
6. arrange
7. advice
8. accomplish
9. assign
10. approve

Challenge Words

1. appropriate
2. admonish
3. accumulate
4. approximate
5. associate

After the Spill

The Prefix *ob-*

ob- ➔ ob-, oc-

object
occur

Spelling Words

1. occur
2. observe
3. obtain
4. oppose
5. object
6. obstruct
7. occupy
8. obvious
9. occasion
10. oppress

Challenge Words

1. opportunity
2. obstacle
3. obnoxious
4. obligation
5. obscure

The Search for the Right Whale

The Prefix *con-*

con- ➔ con-, com-

conduct
command
compare
combine

Spelling Words

1. command
2. conduct
3. convince
4. common
5. compare
6. contain
7. concern
8. combine
9. continue
10. company

Challenge Words

1. conservation
2. commercial
3. contribute
4. competitive
5. consolidate

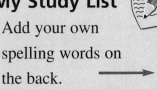

My Study List

Add your own spelling words on the back. ➔

My Study List

Add your own spelling words on the back. ➔

My Study List

Add your own spelling words on the back. ➔

Name _____

 My Study List

1. _____
2. _____
3. _____
4. _____
5. _____
6. _____
7. _____
8. _____
9. _____
10. _____

Selection Vocabulary

You may want to use these words in your own writing.

1. survey
2. essential
3. distinctive
4. consolidate
5. integrate

How to Study a Word

LOOK at the word.
SAY the word.
THINK about the word.
WRITE the word.
CHECK the spelling.

Name _____

 My Study List

1. _____
2. _____
3. _____
4. _____
5. _____
6. _____
7. _____
8. _____
9. _____
10. _____

Selection Vocabulary

You may want to use these words in your own writing.

1. contaminated
2. dispersion
3. microbes
4. chronic

How to Study a Word

LOOK at the word.
SAY the word.
THINK about the word.
WRITE the word.
CHECK the spelling.

Name _____

 My Study List

1. _____
2. _____
3. _____
4. _____
5. _____
6. _____
7. _____
8. _____
9. _____
10. _____

Selection Vocabulary

You may want to use these words in your own writing.

1. boycotting
2. protested
3. campaign
4. presentation
5. targeted
6. public relations
7. image

How to Study a Word

LOOK at the word.
SAY the word.
THINK about the word.
WRITE the word.
CHECK the spelling.

Short Vowels

1. A short vowel sound is usually spelled *a, e, i, o*, or *u* and is followed by a consonant sound.

ask   lo**ck**
n**ex**t   sh**u**t
m**ix**

2. The short *e* sound can be spelled with the pattern *ea*.

m**ea**nt

3. The short *u* sound can be spelled with the pattern *ou* or *o*.

t**ou**ch   n**o**thing

Long Vowel Sounds

4. The long *a* sound can be spelled with the pattern *a*-consonant-*e, ai, ea*, or *ay*.

sc**ale**   gr**ea**t
ch**ai**n   aw**ay**

5. The long *e* sound is often spelled with the pattern *e*-consonant-*e, ea*, or *ee*.

th**ese**   thr**ee**
b**ea**ch

6. The long *e* sound at the end of a word may be spelled *y*.

penn**y**   funn**y**

7. The long *i* sound can be spelled with the pattern *i*-consonant-*e, igh*, or *ie*.

pr**ize**   t**ie**
m**igh**t

8. The long *i* sound at the end of a word may be spelled *y*.

repl**y**

9. The long *o* sound can be spelled with the pattern *o*-consonant-*e, oa*, or *ow*.

th**ose**   **ow**n
fl**oa**t

10. The long *u* sound |yo͞o| or |o͞o| may be spelled with the pattern *u*-consonant-*e, ew, ue, oo, ou*, or *ui*.

r**ule**   r**oo**ts
gr**ew**   gr**ou**p
tr**ue**   fr**ui**t

Other Vowel Sounds

11. The sound |ou| is often spelled with the pattern *ow* or *ou*.

fr**ow**n   pr**ou**d

12. The sound |oi| is spelled with the pattern *oi* or *oy*.

v**oi**ce   b**oy**

13. The vowel sound in *saw* can be spelled with the pattern *a* before *l, aw, au, ough*, or *augh*.

t**a**lk   th**ough**t
awful   c**augh**t
bec**au**se

14. The vowel sound in *cook* may be spelled *oo* or *u*.

w**oo**ds   p**u**ll

15. Use *i* before *e* except after *c* or in words with the long *a* sound, as in *weigh*.

p**ie**ce   **ei**ght
rec**ei**ve

Vowel + *r* Sounds

16. The vowel + *r* sounds you hear in *sharp* can be spelled with the pattern *ar*.

st**ar**tle

17. The vowel + *r* sounds you hear in *hair* can be spelled with the pattern *are* or *air*.

gl**are**   p**air**

18. The vowel + *r* sounds you hear in *peer* can be spelled with the pattern *ear* or *eer*.

f**ear**   st**eer**

19. The vowel + *r* sounds you hear in *roar* can be spelled with the patterns *or*, *ore*, and *oar*.

p**or**ch   s**oar**
bef**ore**

20. The vowel + *r* sounds in *perch* can be spelled with the pattern *er*, *ir*, *ur*, *ear*, or *or*.

w**er**e   **ear**ly
sh**ir**t   w**or**k
b**ur**n

Consonant Sounds

21. The |sh| sound you hear at the beginning of *sheriff* may be spelled with the pattern *sh*, *ti*, *ci*, or *ss*.

a**sh**amed   so**ci**al
emo**ti**on   ti**ss**ue

22. The |s| sound you hear in *city* may be spelled *c* when the *c* is followed by *i* or *e*. The |s| sound at the end of a word is often spelled with the pattern *ce*.

city   pea**ce**
sli**ce**

23. The |j| sound you hear in the word *edge* can be spelled with the consonant *j*, the pattern *dge*, or the pattern *ge*.

just   lar**ge**
e**dge**

Syllable Patterns

24. The schwa + *r* sounds that you hear in *danger* are often spelled with the pattern *er*, *or*, or *ar*.

shiv**er**   li**ar**
terr**or**

25. The schwa + *l* sounds that you hear in *tremble* can be spelled with the pattern *il*, *le*, *el*, or *al*.

gerb**il**   tunn**el**
batt**le**   sever**al**

26. The schwa + *n* sounds that you hear in *weapon* can be spelled with the pattern *on* or *en*.

reas**on**   hidd**en**

27. The schwa + *nt* sounds that you hear in *pleasant* can be spelled with the pattern *ant* or *ent*.

brilli**ant**
differ**ent**

28. The schwa + *ns* sounds that you hear in *difference* can be spelled *-ance* or *-ence*.

appear**ance**
sent**ence**

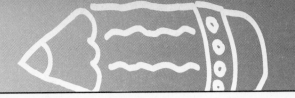

Find the syllables in two-syllable words by looking for spelling patterns you have learned. Spell the words by syllables.

29. Some two-syllable words have the vowel-consonant-vowel pattern (VCV), and begin with the short vowel pattern. Divide these words after the consonant to find the syllables.

min|ute
prom|ise

30. Some two-syllable words have the vowel-consonant-vowel pattern (VCV), and the first syllable is unstressed or ends with a long vowel sound. Divide these words before the consonant to find the syllables.

re|fuse
la|bor

31. Some two-syllable words have the vowel-consonant-consonant-vowel pattern (VCCV). Divide these words between the two consonants to find the syllables.

ab|sent
whis|per

32. Some two-syllable words have the vowel-consonant-consonant-consonant-vowel (VCCCV) pattern. In these words, when two different consonants spell one sound, as in *trophy*, or form a cluster, as in *empty*, divide these words into syllables before or after those two consonants.

VC|CCV	VCC|CV
in|stead	laugh|ter
ap|plaud	emp|ty

Word Endings

33. If a base word ends with *e*, drop the *e* before adding the ending *-ed* or *-ing*.

shap**e** - shap**ed**
ris**e** - ris**ing**

34. If a one-syllable base word ends with one vowel and one consonant, double the consonant before *-ed* or *-ing*.

wrap**ped**
slip**ping**

35. When a two-syllable base word ends with a stressed syllable, double the final consonant before *-ed* or *-ing*.

be<u>gin</u> - begin**ning**
<u>cov</u>er - cover**ed**

36. When a base word ends with a consonant and *y*, change the *y* to *i* before adding *-es, -ed, -er, -est,* or *-ness.*

sk**y** - sk**ies**
tr**y** - tr**ied**
angr**y** - angr**ier**, angr**iest**
happ**y** - happ**iness**

37. Words that end with the final sound in *realize* can be spelled with the pattern *-ize* or *-ise.*

critic**ize**   advert**ise**

38. Add *-s* to most words to name more than one. Add *-es* to words ending in *s, x, sh,* or *ch.*
See also page 320 for more rules for forming plural nouns.

bus**es**   wish**es**
box**es**   peach**es**

SPELLING GUIDELINES

Prefixes and Suffixes

39. A **prefix** is a word part that is added to the beginning of a base word or a word root.

reread   **ex**cept
unfair   **con**fuse
dislike   **com**pete

40. When the **prefix** *ad-* is added before the letter *c, r,* or *s,* the *d* changes to match those letters.

accuse   **as**sume
arrive

41. The **prefix** *ob-* is spelled *oc-* before the consonant *c.*

occur   **oc**casion

42. The **prefix** *con-* is often spelled *com* before the consonant *m, p,* or *b.*

command   **com**bine
compare

43. A **suffix** is a word part that is added to the end of a base word or a word root.

lov**able**   good**ness**
writ**er**   thought**ful**

44. When adding the **suffix** *-able* to a root word ending with *s* or *d,* the suffix is spelled *-ible.*

vis**ible**   incred**ible**

45. When a **suffix** begins with a vowel, the final *e* is usually dropped from the base word. When the suffix begins with a consonant, the final *e* is usually kept.

writ**e** - writ**er**
clos**e** - clos**eness**

46. When the suffix *-ly* is added to a base word ending with the lĬl or lₐll sounds spelled *le,* the final *le* is dropped.

simp**le** - simp**ly**

47. A noun is formed when the **suffix** *-ion* or *-ation* is added to a verb. When the verb ends with *e,* drop the *e* before adding *-ion* or *-ation.*

construct - construct**ion**
inform - inform**ation**
locat**e** - locat**ion**
explor**e** - explor**ation**

48. If a verb ends with the final *d* sound, the *d* changes to another consonant when *-ion* is added.

deci**de** - deci**sion**
inten**d** - inten**tion**

Special Spellings

49. **Homophones** are words that sound alike but have different meanings and spellings.

threw - through
waste - waist

50. In **contractions**, an apostrophe takes the place of the letters that are dropped.

haven't
shouldn't

51. A **compound word** is made up of two or more smaller words. It can be written as one word, as words joined by a hyphen, or as separate words.

teenager
old-fashioned
living room

52. **Silent consonants** are consonants that are not pronounced.

wrong   is**l**and   **h**onest
pa**l**m   of**t**en   **kn**ew

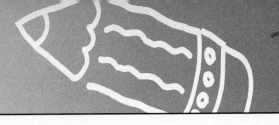

SENTENCES

Definition

A **sentence** is a group of words that expresses a complete thought. It has a subject (who or what) and a predicate (what the subject does or is). A sentence begins with a capital letter.

> **L**ightning flashed in the sky.   **T**he alert ranger spotted fire.

- A group of words that does not express a complete thought is called a **sentence fragment**. A fragment is not a sentence.

> Flashed in the sky.   When the tree fell.

Kinds of Sentences

There are four kinds of sentences.

- A **declarative sentence** makes a statement, or tells something. It ends with a period.
> **D**eserts are dry**.**

- An **interrogative sentence** asks a question. It ends with a question mark.
> **D**o you like deserts**?**

- An **imperative sentence** gives a command or makes a request. It ends with a period.
> **A**lways carry water**.**

- An **exclamatory sentence** expresses excitement or strong feeling. It ends with an exclamation point.
> **H**ow hot it was**!**   **I**t was so hot**!**

Subjects and Predicates

Every sentence has a **subject** and a **predicate.**

- The **subject** tells whom or what the sentence is about. The **complete subject** includes all the words in the subject. It may be one or more words.
> **The pilots of the plane** waved.   **They** were preparing for takeoff.

- The **simple subject** is the main word or words in the complete subject.
> **The <u>pilots</u> of the plane** waved.   <u>**South America**</u> is their destination.

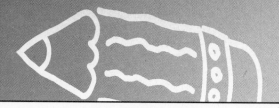
Subjects and Predicates (continued)

- In an imperative sentence, the subject *you* is understood.

    (You) Please bring your camera.

- To find the subject of an interrogative sentence, rearrange the question into a statement. Then ask *who* or *what* does the action.

    Will they take a picture?   They will take a picture.

- The **predicate** tells what the subject is or does. The **complete predicate** includes all the words in the predicate. It may be either one word or more than one word.

    Captain Ortega **is a good pilot**.   The large jet **landed**.

- The **simple predicate** is the main word or words in the complete predicate. It is always a verb, a word that shows action or being.

    Several helicopters **landed there**.   They **have landed** there before.

Run-on Sentences

A **run-on sentence** is two or more sentences run together incorrectly into one sentence.

- Correct a run-on sentence by writing each complete thought as a separate sentence.

    RUN-ON: Electricians often wear rubber gloves electricity cannot go through rubber.

    CORRECTED: Electricians often wear rubber gloves. Electricity cannot go through rubber.

- Correct a run-on sentence by making it into a compound sentence (two sentences joined by a comma and a connecting word like *and, or,* or *but*) or a compound sentence and a short sentence. In a compound sentence, the two parts should be related.

    RUN-ON: Some jobs require special clothing these clothes provide protection.

    CORRECTED: Some jobs require special clothing, **and** these clothes provide protection.

    RUN-ON: Some firefighters wear flameproof suits the suits are coated with metal they totally cover the firefighter.

    CORRECTED: Some firefighters wear flameproof suits. (*short*) The suits are coated with metal, **and** they totally cover the firefighter. (*compound*)

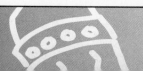

NOUNS

Definition

A **noun** names a person, a place, a thing, or an idea.

Nouns			
Persons	boy	student	Li Chen
Places	lake	Fenway Park	mountain
Things	boat	calendar	*Little Women*
Ideas	truth	freedom	happiness

Common and Proper Nouns

A **common noun** names any person, place, thing, or idea. A **proper noun** names a particular person, place, thing, or idea. Capitalize proper nouns. Capitalize each important word in proper nouns of more than one word.

Common and Proper Nouns			
Common nouns	**Proper nouns**	**Common nouns**	**Proper nouns**
street	North Drive	river	Hudson River
city	Vancouver	ocean	Arctic Ocean
state	Maryland	mountain	Mt. McKinley
continent	Asia	lake	Great Salt Lake

Singular and Plural Nouns

Singular nouns name one person, place, thing, or idea.

The **farmer** drove to the **market** with the **box**.

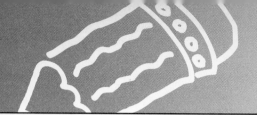
Singular and Plural Nouns (continued)

Plural nouns name more than one person, place, thing, or idea.

    The **farmers** drove to the **markets** with the **boxes**.

- Form the plural of most nouns by adding *s* or *es*. Look at the ending of a singular noun to decide how to form the plural. Some nouns have special plural forms.

Rules for Forming Plural Nouns				
Most singular nouns: Add *s*.	street	street**s**	house	house**s**
Nouns ending with *s*, *x*, *ch*, or *sh*: Add *es*.	dress ax	dress**es** ax**es**	bench dish	bench**es** dish**es**
Nouns ending with a vowel and *y*: Add *s*.	valley	valley**s**	joy	joy**s**
Nouns ending with a consonant and *y*: Change the *y* to *i* and add *es*.	city	cit**ies**	cranberry	cranberr**ies**
Nouns ending in *f* or *fe*: Change the *f* to *v* and add *es* to some nouns. Add *s* to others.	life calf	li**ves** cal**ves**	roof cliff	roof**s** cliff**s**
Nouns ending with a vowel and *o*: Add *s*.	rodeo studio	rodeo**s** studio**s**	radio	radio**s**
Nouns ending with a consonant and *o*: Add *s* to some nouns. Add *es* to other nouns.	solo piano	solo**s** piano**s**	hero echo	hero**es** echo**es**
Nouns that have special plural spellings	woman mouse	wom**en** m**ice**	foot ox	f**ee**t ox**en**
Nouns that remain the same in the singular and the plural	sheep moose	sheep moose	trout deer	trout deer

Singular and Plural Possessive Nouns

A **possessive noun** names *who* or *what* has or owns something.

- To form the possessive of a singular noun, add an apostrophe and *s*.

  the car**'s** tires   a student**'s** papers   Rosa**'s** opinion

- To form the possessive of a plural noun that ends with *s*, add only an apostrophe.

  the cars**'** horns   two students**'** books   two girls**'** ideas

- To form the possessive of a plural noun that does not end with *s*, add an apostrophe and *s*.

  the children**'s** choice   the oxen**'s** tracks   the people**'s** cheers

VERBS

Definition

A **verb** is a word that shows action or a state of being. It is the main word or words in the predicate of a sentence.

      ACTION: The fire **burns** brightly.   BEING: It **is** warm.

Main Verbs and Helping Verbs

A verb may be one word or a group of words.

      The coach **blew** the whistle.   The runners **have started** the race.

- A **verb phrase** is made up of a main verb and helping verb. The **main verb** shows the action. A **helping verb** works with the main verb and comes before the main verb.

  helping verb   main verb
  Kiran **has passed** everyone.

  helping verb   main verb
  He **has been running** hard.

Common Helping Verbs

am	are	were	shall	has
is	was	will	have	had

Action Verbs and Direct Objects

An **action verb** shows what the subject does or did. Action verbs can also show action that you cannot see.

> Roberta **swings** at the ball.   The coach **thought** about the players in the field.

A **direct object** is a noun or a pronoun in the predicate that receives the action of the verb. When an action verb has a direct object, the verb is called a **transitive verb**.

- Direct objects follow action verbs only and answer the question *what* or *whom*.
  The captain steers the big **ship**. (steers what? steers the big **ship**)
  The captain calls the **crew**. (calls whom? calls the **crew**)

- An action verb does not always have a direct object. Then the verb is called an **intransitive verb**.
  The ship sails.   The ship sails across the ocean.

Being Verbs and Linking Verbs

A being verb is often a **linking verb**. A linking verb links the subject of a sentence with a word or words in the predicate that name or describe the subject. If the word names or identifies the subject, it is a **predicate noun**. If it describes the subject, it is a **predicate adjective**.

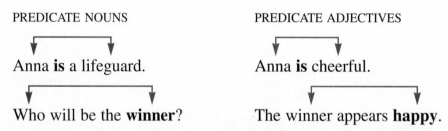

PREDICATE NOUNS

Anna **is** a lifeguard.

Who will be the **winner**?

PREDICATE ADJECTIVES

Anna **is** cheerful.

The winner appears **happy**.

Common Linking Verbs

am	is	are	was	were	will be
look	feel	taste	smell	seem	appear

Being Verbs and Linking Verbs (continued)

- A linking verb can be more than one word.

  We <u>are feeling</u> happy.   They <u>are looking</u> tired.

- Some verbs can be either linking verbs or action verbs.

  LINKING: The soup **tastes** salty.

  ACTION: I **taste** the salt in this soup.

Verb Tense

The **tense** of the verb lets you know whether something happens in the present, the past, or the future.

  PRESENT: Bats **hunt** at night.

  PAST: They **hunted** last night.

  FUTURE: They **will hunt** tonight also.

Present Tense

A **present tense verb** shows action that is happening now.

- A subject and its verb must agree in number. Singular subjects take singular verbs. Plural subjects take plural verbs.

- Use a plural verb with a compound subject joined by *and*.

Rules for Subject-Verb Agreement

Singular subject: Add *s* or *es* to the verb.	The driver trai**ns** his dogs. He teach**es** one dog to lead.	He studi**es** his map.
Plural subject or *I* or *you*: Do not add *s* or *es* to the verb.	The **dogs pull** the sleds. The **drivers and dogs travel** far. **They work** together.	**I like** your report on dogs. **You write** well.

Present Tense (continued)

- Change the spelling of some verbs when adding *s* or *es*.

Rules for Forming Present Tense Singular Verbs

Most verbs: Add *s*.	get - get**s**	play - play**s**
Verbs ending with *s*, *ch*, *sh*, *x*, and *z*: Add *es*.	pass - pass**es** punch - punch**es** push - push**es**	mix - mix**es** fizz - fizz**es**
Verbs ending with a consonant and *y*: Change the *y* to *i* and add *es*.	try - tr**ies** empty - empt**ies**	carry - carr**ies** supply - suppl**ies**

Past Tense

A **past tense verb** shows that something already happened. Form the past tense of most verbs by adding *-ed*.

> We **cooked** our dinner over a campfire last night.

- Change the spelling of some verbs when adding *-ed*.

Rules for Forming the Past Tense

Most verbs: Add *-ed*.	play - play**ed** reach - reach**ed**
Verbs ending with *e*: Drop the *e* and add *-ed*.	believe - believ**ed** hope - hop**ed**
Verbs ending with a consonant and *y*: Change the *y* to *i* and add *-ed*.	stu**dy** - stud**ied** hur**ry** - hurr**ied**
Verbs ending with a single vowel and a consonant: Double the final consonant and add *-ed*.	stop - sto**pped** plan - pla**nned**

Future Tense

A **future tense verb** tells what is going to happen. Use the main verb with the helping verb *will* or *shall* to form the future tense.

> Wen **will bring** his bird book tomorrow.
> Wen and I **will look** for some nests.
> **Shall** we **invite** Melissa?

Verb Tenses with *be* and *have*

Be and *have* have special forms in the present and past tenses. Change the forms of *be* and *have* to agree with their subjects.

Subject	Form of *be*		Form of *have*	
	Present	**Past**	**Present**	**Past**
Singular subjects:				
I	am	was	have	had
you	are	were	have	had
he, she, it, or singular noun	is	was	has	had
Plural subjects:				
we, plural noun, *you, they*	are	were	have	had

Principal Parts of Verbs

The **principal parts,** or basic forms, of a verb are the verb, the present participle, the past, and the past participle. All the tenses of a verb come from these four forms.

Irregular Verbs

The past and past participle of some verbs are not formed by adding *-ed*. These verbs are irregular. **Irregular verbs** have special forms to show the past.

Principal Parts of Irregular Verbs

Verb	Present participle	Past	Past participle
be	(is) being	was	(has) been
blow	(is) blowing	blew	(has) blown
bring	(is) bringing	brought	(has) brought
choose	(is) choosing	chose	(has) chosen
come	(is) coming	came	(has) come
do	(is) doing	did	(has) done
drive	(is) driving	drove	(has) driven
go	(is) going	went	(has) gone
grow	(is) growing	grew	(has) grown
have	(is) having	had	(has) had
know	(is) knowing	knew	(has) known
lend	(is) lending	lent	(has) lent
make	(is) making	made	(has) made
ride	(is) riding	rode	(has) ridden
run	(is) running	ran	(has) run
say	(is) saying	said	(has) said
see	(is) seeing	saw	(has) seen
speak	(is) speaking	spoke	(has) spoken
steal	(is) stealing	stole	(has) stolen
swim	(is) swimming	swam	(has) swum
take	(is) taking	took	(has) taken
tear	(is) tearing	tore	(has) torn
think	(is) thinking	thought	(has) thought
throw	(is) throwing	threw	(has) thrown
wear	(is) wearing	wore	(has) worn
write	(is) writing	wrote	(has) written

ADJECTIVES

Definition

An **adjective** is a word that describes a noun or a pronoun.

> **Powerful** lions stared at us.   They seemed **irritated**.

- An adjective tells *what kind*, *which one*, or *how many*. It can come before a noun or after a linking verb.

what kind	**Spotted** fawns were resting.	They looked **peaceful**.
how many	**Three** elephants were eating.	Monkeys did **several** tricks.
which one	**That** bear went into its den.	**Those** cubs played together.

- When two or more adjectives are listed together, use a comma to separate them, unless one of the adjectives tells *how many*.

> **Large, colorful** parrots screeched. **Two white** geese honked loudly.

Articles

A, *an*, and *the* are special adjectives called **articles**. *A* and *an* refer to any person, place, thing, or idea. *The* refers to a particular person, place, thing, or idea.

> Let's take **a** trip. (any)   It's time for **the** trip. (particular)

Articles	
a	Use before singular words that begin with a consonant sound. **a** jet **a** high step
an	Use before singular words that begin with a vowel sound. **an** engineer **an** hour
the	Use before singular and plural words. **the** answer **the** plans

GRAMMAR GUIDE

Demonstrative Adjectives

Adjectives that tell *which one* are called **demonstrative adjectives**. They point out a specific person, place, or thing. *This, that, these,* and *those* are demonstrative adjectives.

- *This* and *these* refer to nouns close to the speaker or writer. *That* and *those* refer to nouns farther away.

    This book is my favorite.   **That** book is Aja's favorite.

- *This* and *that* are used with singular nouns. *These* and *those* are used with plural nouns.

Demonstrative Adjectives		
	Singular	**Plural**
Things that are close	this	these
Things that are farther away	that	those

Comparing with Adjectives

To compare two people, places, things, or ideas, use the **comparative** form of the adjective. Add *-er* to most adjectives. To compare three or more, use the **superlative** form. Add *-est.* Use *more* and *most,* not *-er* and *-est,* with most long adjectives.

ONE PERSON: My brother is **tall**. He seems **gigantic**.

TWO PERSONS: My mother is **taller** than my brother. She seems **more gigantic** than he does.

THREE OR MORE: My father is **tallest** of all. He seems **most gigantic**.

Comparing with Adjectives (continued)

- Change the spelling of some adjectives when adding *-er* and *-est*.

Rules for Comparing with Adjectives

Most adjectives: Add *-er* or *-est* to the adjective.	bright bright**er** bright**est**
Adjectives ending with *e*: Drop the *e* and add *-er* or *-est*.	saf**e** saf**er** saf**est**
Adjectives ending with a consonant and *y*: Change the *y* to *i* and add *-er* or *-est*.	bus**y** bus**ier** bus**iest**
One-syllable adjectives that end with a single vowel and a consonant: Double the final consonant and add *-er* or *-est*.	fl**at** flat**ter** flat**test**
Most adjectives of two or more syllables: Use *more* or *most* instead of *-er* or *-est*.	careful **more** careful **most** careful

The adjectives *good, bad, much,* and *little* are irregular. They have completely different forms to show the comparative and the superlative.

> This artist is <u>better</u> than that one. *(comparative)*
> The green paint is <u>worse</u> than the red. *(comparative)*
> Which artist has painted the <u>most</u> pictures? *(superlative)*
> Who has the <u>least</u> experience? *(superlative)*

Comparing with Adjectives (continued)

Adjective	Comparative	Superlative
much	more	most
little	less	least
good	better	best
bad	worse	worst

ADVERBS

Definition

An **adverb** is a word that describes a verb, an adjective, or another adverb.

- Adverbs that describe verbs tell *how, when, where,* or *to what extent.*

- Adverbs that describe adjectives or other adverbs tell *how* or *to what extent.*

HOW: The plane landed **smoothly** at the airport.

WHEN: **Soon** Jeff would see his grandparents at the gate.

WHERE: They were waiting for him **there**.

TO WHAT EXTENT: They **really** enjoyed his visits.

Jeff spotted them **almost** immediately.

Adverbs (continued)

How	When	Where	To What Extent
fast	tomorrow	here	very
hard	later	inside	slightly
together	again	far	quite
happily	often	upstairs	too
quietly	first	downtown	terribly
secretly	next	somewhere	almost
slowly	then	forward	rather

Comparing with Adverbs

Like adjectives, adverbs can be used to make comparisons. To compare two things, use the comparative form (*-er*). To compare more than two things, use the superlative form (*-est*). Use *more* or *most* with long adverbs or with most adverbs ending with *-ly*.

Rules for Forming the Comparative and Superlative Forms of Adverbs

Most short adverbs: Add *-er* or *-est* to the adverb.	late early la**ter** earli**er** la**test** earli**est**
Most adverbs of two or more syllables: Use *more* or *most* with the adverb.	often quickly **more** often **more** quickly **most** often **most** quickly
Some adverbs become completely new words.	well badly little much better worse less more best worst least most

Comparing with Adverbs (continued)

ADVERB: Amy will finish the book **soon**.

She will return the book **promptly**.

She does not need **much** more time.

COMPARATIVE: Amy will finish **sooner** than Jessie will.

She will return the book **more promptly** than Jessie will.

Jessie is **less** likely to finish the book this week.

SUPERLATIVE: Amy will finish **soonest** of all.

She will return the book **most promptly** of all.

Amy enjoyed this book **most**.

- Never use *-er* with *more*. Never use *-est* with *most*.

INCORRECT: Leslie skates **more smoother** than Roberto.

CORRECT: Leslie skates **more smoothly** than Roberto.

INCORRECT: Denzel works the **most hardest** of all the students.

CORRECT: Denzel works the **hardest** of all the students.

PRONOUNS

Definition

A **pronoun** is a word that takes the place of a noun.

Carl watches the swimmers.   The swimmers listen for the whistle.

He watches **them**.   **They** listen for **it**.

The **antecedent** of a pronoun is the noun or nouns to which the pronoun refers. The antecedent does not have to be in the same sentence as the pronoun.

When Mary won the blue ribbon, <u>she</u> smiled happily.

The audience clapped loudly for her dive. <u>It</u> was perfect.

Subject Pronouns

There are seven **subject pronouns**. Some are singular, and some are plural.

Subject Pronouns	
Singular	**Plural**
I	we
you	you
he, she, it	they

- Use a **subject pronoun** to replace a noun used as the subject of a sentence.

  I would like to compete in a swimming race.

  You offered some tips.

  They have helped improve my speed.

- Use a **subject pronoun** to replace a noun used after a form of the verb *be*.

  The first swimmer into the water was **I**.

  Did Tina and Angelo win? Yes, the winners were **they**.

- Use a **subject pronoun** in a compound subject. When using *I* with another noun or subject pronoun, always name yourself last.

  Mario and I go to every swim meet.

  The ticket takers at the last meet were **Letty and I**.

Object Pronouns

There are seven **object pronouns**. Some are singular, and some are plural. (Note that *it* and *you* may be subject or object pronouns.)

Object Pronouns	
Singular	**Plural**
me	us
you	you
him, her, it	them

- Use an **object pronoun** to replace a noun used as a direct object after an action verb.

    Dad started to build a campfire. Rebecca helped **him**.

    They built **it** inside a circle of stones.

- Use an **object pronoun** to replace a noun after words such as *to, for, about, between,* and *after.*

    Will Jeremy cook dinner <u>for</u> **us**?

    Arlyn will give the meat <u>to</u> **me**.

    I will eat <u>after</u> **you**.

- Use an **object pronoun** in a compound object. When using *me* with another noun or with an object pronoun, always name yourself last.

    Dad showed **Jeremy and me** how to fish.

    The fish weren't biting for **him and me**.

The Pronouns *who, whom, whose*

Use the pronoun *who* as a subject.   *Who* is the singer?

Use the pronoun *whom* as a direct object.   *Whom* did you choose as your favorite?

Use the pronoun *whose* to show ownership.   *Whose* tickets are these?

Indefinite Pronouns

An **indefinite pronoun** does not refer to a specific person or thing. When you use an indefinite pronoun as a subject, the verb must agree with it.

- A singular indefinite pronoun takes a singular verb.

    <u>Everyone</u> is invited.   <u>Neither</u> is here.

- A plural indefinite pronoun takes a plural verb.

    <u>Several</u> were invited.   <u>Many</u> are here.

Indefinite Pronouns

Singular			Plural	
anybody	everybody	nothing	all	others
anyone	everyone	somebody	both	several
anything	everything	someone	few	some
each	nobody	something	many	

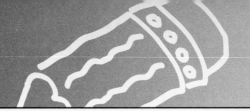

GRAMMAR GUIDE

PREPOSITIONS AND PREPOSITIONAL PHRASES

Definition

A **preposition** relates the noun or the pronoun that follows it to another word in the sentence.

I liked the book <u>with</u> the blue cover.   Sula gave it <u>to</u> me.

Common Prepositions

about	below	in	through
above	beneath	inside	throughout
across	beside	into	to
after	between	near	toward
against	beyond	of	under
along	by	off	until
around	down	on	up
as	during	out	with
at	except	outside	without
before	for	over	
behind	from	past	

Prepositional Phrases

A **prepositional phrase** is made up of a preposition, the object of the preposition, and the modifiers of the object.

prep.   obj. of prep.

We packed the fruit <u>in our knapsacks</u>.

Prepositional Phrases (continued)

The **object of the preposition** is the noun or the object pronoun that follows the preposition.

prep.   obj. of prep.

I liked the book <u>with the blue **cover**</u>.

prep. obj. of prep.

Sula gave it <u>to **me**</u>.

- The object of the preposition can be a compound object.

  We took enough oranges for <u>Manuel and Anita</u>.

- Use only object pronouns as objects of prepositions. Check the pronoun in a compound object by removing the other object.

  Jim sat <u>with Ann and **me**</u>. (*Think:* Jim sat <u>with **me**</u>.)

- A prepositional phrase can be at the beginning, middle, or end of a sentence.

  <u>At dawn</u> we began our walk.   The map <u>of the area</u> helped us.

  The path went <u>by a forest and a large lake</u>.

Prepositional Phrases as Adjectives

A prepositional phrase can act as an adjective and describe a noun or a pronoun. An **adjective phrase** can tell *what kind* or *which one*.

Everyone <u>in the gym</u> is cheering.   The door <u>to the building</u> is locked.

Prepositional Phrases as Adverbs

A prepositional phrase can act as an adverb and describe a verb, an adjective, or another adverb. An **adverb phrase** can tell *how, where,* or *when*.

Sue ran <u>toward the lake</u>. (modifies verb)

Ted was eager <u>for the race</u>. (modifies adjective)

Melanie swims early <u>in the morning</u>. (modifies adverb)

ABBREVIATIONS

Abbreviations are shortened forms of words. Most abbreviations begin with a capital letter and end with a period. Some have no period. Others have neither capital letters nor periods. Use abbreviations only in special kinds of writing, such as addresses and lists.

- **Titles**

Mr. *(Mister)* Mr. Pedro Arupe	Sr. *(Senior)* James Morton, Sr.
Mrs. *(Mistress)* Mrs. Jane Chang	Jr. *(Junior)* James Morton, Jr.
Ms. Carla Tower	Dr. *(Doctor)* Dr. Ellen Masters

Note: *Miss* is not an abbreviation and does not end with a period.

- **Words Used in Addresses**

St. *(Street)*	Blvd. *(Boulevard)*	Pkwy. *(Parkway)*
Rd. *(Road)*	Rte. *(Route)*	Mt. *(Mount* or *Mountain)*
Ave. *(Avenue)*	Apt. *(Apartment)*	Expy. *(Expressway)*
Dr. *(Drive)*		

- **Words Used in Business**

Co. *(Company)*	Inc. *(Incorporated)*
Corp. *(Corporation)*	Ltd. *(Limited)*

- **Other Abbreviations**

Some abbreviations are written in all capital letters, with a letter standing for each important word.

P.D. *(Police Department)*	P.O. *(Post Office)*
J.P. *(Justice of the Peace)*	R.N. *(Registered Nurse)*
D.V.M. *(Doctor of Veterinary Medicine)*	

ABBREVIATIONS (continued)

- ### States

  The United States Postal Service uses two capital letters and no period in each of its state abbreviations.

AL *(Alabama)*	LA *(Louisiana)*	OH *(Ohio)*
AK *(Alaska)*	ME *(Maine)*	OK *(Oklahoma)*
AZ *(Arizona)*	MD *(Maryland)*	OR *(Oregon)*
AR *(Arkansas)*	MA *(Massachusetts)*	PA *(Pennsylvania)*
CA *(California)*	MI *(Michigan)*	RI *(Rhode Island)*
CO *(Colorado)*	MN *(Minnesota)*	SC *(South Carolina)*
CT *(Connecticut)*	MS *(Mississippi)*	SD *(South Dakota)*
DE *(Delaware)*	MO *(Missouri)*	TN *(Tennessee)*
FL *(Florida)*	MT *(Montana)*	TX *(Texas)*
GA *(Georgia)*	NE *(Nebraska)*	UT *(Utah)*
HI *(Hawaii)*	NV *(Nevada)*	VT *(Vermont)*
ID *(Idaho)*	NH *(New Hampshire)*	VA *(Virginia)*
IL *(Illinois)*	NJ *(New Jersey)*	WA *(Washington)*
IN *(Indiana)*	NM *(New Mexico)*	WV *(West Virginia)*
IA *(Iowa)*	NY *(New York)*	WI *(Wisconsin)*
KS *(Kansas)*	NC *(North Carolina)*	WY *(Wyoming)*
KY *(Kentucky)*	ND *(North Dakota)*	

- ### Initials

  Initials are abbreviations that stand for a person's first or middle name. Some names have both a first and a middle initial.

  E.B. White *(Elwyn Brooks White)*

  T. James Carey *(Thomas James Carey)*

  Mr. John M. Gordon *(Mister John Morris Gordon)*

TITLES

Underlining

The important words and the first and last words in a title are capitalized. Titles of books, magazines, TV shows, movies, and newspapers are underlined.

<u>The Call of the Wild</u> (book)   <u>Cricket</u> (magazine)   <u>Nova</u> (TV show)

<u>Treasure Island</u> (movie)   <u>The Phoenix Express</u> (newspaper)

Computer Tip: Use italic type for these kinds of titles instead of underlining.

Quotation Marks with Titles

Titles of short stories, songs, articles, book chapters, and most poems are set off by quotation marks.

"The Necklace" (short story)   "Home on the Range" (song)

"Three Days in the Sahara" (article)   "The Human Brain" (chapter)

"Deer at Dusk" (poem)

QUOTATIONS

Quotation Marks with Commas and Periods

Quotation marks set off a speaker's exact words. Begin the first word of a quotation with a capital letter. Place punctuation *inside* the closing quotation marks. Use commas to separate most quotations from the rest of the sentence.

"Where," asked the stranger, "is the post office?"

"Please put away your books now," said Mr. Emory.

Linda whispered, "What time is it?"

"It's late," replied Bill. "Let's go!"

Writing a Conversation

Begin a new paragraph each time a new person begins speaking.

"Are you going to drive all the way to Columbus in one day?" asked my Uncle Ben.

"I really haven't decided," said my father. "I was hoping that you would share the driving with me."

CAPITALIZATION

1. Capitalize the first word of every sentence.
   <u>W</u>hat a wonderful day this is!

2. Capitalize the pronoun *I*.
   What can <u>I</u> do this afternoon?

3. Capitalize proper nouns. If a proper noun is made up of more than one word, capitalize each important word.
   Emily <u>G</u>. <u>M</u>esse District of <u>C</u>olumbia Lincoln <u>M</u>emorial

4. Capitalize titles or their abbreviations when used with a person's name.
   <u>G</u>overnor <u>B</u>radford <u>S</u>enator <u>S</u>mith <u>D</u>r. <u>L</u>ing

5. Capitalize family titles when they are used as names or as part of names.
   We called <u>A</u>unt Leslie. May we leave now, <u>G</u>randpa?

6. Capitalize proper adjectives.
   We ate at a <u>F</u>rench restaurant.
   She is <u>G</u>erman.
   That is a <u>N</u>orth <u>A</u>merican custom.

7. Capitalize the names of days, months, and holidays.
   The meeting is on the first <u>T</u>uesday in <u>M</u>ay.
   We watched the parade on the <u>F</u>ourth of <u>J</u>uly.

GRAMMAR GUIDE

CAPITALIZATION (continued)

8. Capitalize the names of groups.

Aspen Mountain Club   International League

9. Capitalize the names of buildings and companies.

Empire State Building   Able Supply Company
Central School

10. Capitalize the first, last, and all important words in a title. Do not capitalize words such as *a, in, and, of,* and *the* unless they begin or end a title.

Secrets of a Wildlife Watcher   "Growing Up"
The Los Angeles Times

11. Capitalize the first word in the greeting and the closing of a letter.

Dear Marcia,   Sincerely yours,

12. Capitalize the first word of each main topic and subtopic in an outline.

I. Types of fire departments
    A. Full-time departments
    B. Volunteer departments

PUNCTUATION

End Marks

There are three end marks. A *period* (.) ends a declarative or imperative sentence. A *question mark* (?) follows an interrogative sentence. An *exclamation point* (!) follows an exclamatory sentence.

The notebook is on the shelf. *(declarative)*
Watch that program at eight tonight. *(imperative)*
Where does the trail end? *(interrogative)*
This is your best poem so far! *(exclamatory)*

Apostrophe

To form the possessive of a singular noun, add an apostrophe and *s*.

>   doctor's   grandfather's
>   James's   community's

For a plural noun that ends in *s*, add only an apostrophe.

>   sisters'   families'
>   students'   hound dogs'
>   Boltons'

For a plural noun that does not end in *s*, add an apostrophe and *s* to form the plural possessive.

>   geese's   children's
>   men's   mice's

Use an apostrophe in place of dropped letters in contractions. Do not use contractions in formal writing.

isn't *(is not)*	I'm *(I am)*
can't *(cannot)*	they've *(they have)*
won't *(will not)*	they'll *(they will)*
wasn't *(was not)*	could've *(could have)*
we're *(we are)*	would've *(would have)*
it's *(it is)*	should've *(should have)*

Colon

Use a colon after the greeting in a business letter.

>   Dear Mrs. Trimby: Dear Realty Homes:

Comma

A comma tells your reader where to pause.

1. Use commas to separate words or groups of words in a series. Use a comma before the conjunction *and* or *or* that connects the items.

    We made a salad of lettuce, peppers, and tomatoes.
    We ate lunch, went for a walk, and played ball.

2. Use commas to separate two or more adjectives that are listed together unless one adjective tells *how many*.

    The fresh, ripe fruit was placed in a bowl.
    One red apple was especially shiny.

3. Use a comma to separate the simple sentences in a compound sentence.

    Some students were at lunch, but others were studying.

4. Use a comma after introductory words, such as *yes, no, oh,* and *well*.

    Yes, it's a perfect day for a picnic.   Well, I'll make dessert.

5. Use commas to separate a noun in direct address.

    Gloria, hold this light for me.   Can you see, Joe, where I left my glasses?
    How was the movie, Grandma?

6. Use a comma to separate the month and the day from the year. Use a comma to separate the year from the rest of the sentence.

    He was born on July 3, 1981.
    July 4, 1776, is the birthday of our nation.

7. Use a comma between the names of a city and a state.

    Denver, Colorado   Miami, Florida

8. Use a comma after the greeting in a friendly letter.

    Dear Tayo,   Dear Aunt Claudia,

9. Use a comma after the closing in a letter.

    Your friend,   Yours truly,

Quotation Marks See Quotations, pp. 340–341.

PROBLEM WORDS

Words	Rules	Examples
bad	*Bad* is an adjective. It can be used after linking verbs like *look* and *feel*.	This was a bad day. I feel bad.
badly	*Badly* is an adverb.	I play badly.
borrow lend	*Borrow* means "to take." *Lend* means "to give."	You may borrow my pen. I will lend it to you for the day.
can	*Can* means "to be able to do something."	Nellie can read quickly.
may	*May* means "to be allowed or permitted."	May I borrow your book?
good well	*Good* is an adjective. *Well* is usually an adverb. It is an adjective only when it refers to health.	The weather looks good. She sings well. Do you feel well?
in into	*In* means "located within." *Into* means "movement from the outside to the inside."	Your lunch is in that bag. He jumped into the pool.
its it's	*Its* is a possessive pronoun. *It's* is a contraction of *it is*.	The dog wagged its tail. It's cold today.
let leave	*Let* means "to permit or allow." *Leave* means "to go away from" or "to let remain in a place."	Please let me go swimming. I will leave soon. Leave it on my desk.
lie lay	*Lie* means "to rest or recline." *Lay* means "to put or place something."	The dog lies in its bed. Please lay the books here.
sit	*Sit* means "to rest in one place."	Please sit in this chair.
set	*Set* means "to place or put."	Set the vase on the table.
teach	*Teach* means "to give instruction."	He teaches us how to dance.
learn	*Learn* means "to receive instruction."	I learned about history.

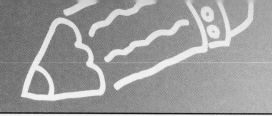

GRAMMAR GUIDE

PROBLEM WORDS (continued)

Words	Rules	Examples
their there they're	*Their* is a possessive pronoun. *There* is an adverb. It may also begin a sentence. *They're* is a contraction of *they are*.	Their coats are on the bed. Is Carlos there? There is my book. They're going to the store.
two to too	*Two* is a number. *To* means "in the direction of." *Too* means "more than enough" and "also."	I bought two shirts. A squirrel ran to the tree. May we go too?
whose who's	*Whose* is a possessive pronoun. *Who's* is a contraction for *who is*.	Whose tickets are these? Who's that woman?
your you're	*Your* is a possessive pronoun. *You're* is a contraction for *you are*.	Are these your glasses? You're late again!

ADVERB USAGE (See also Comparing with Adverbs, pp. 331–332.)

Negatives

A negative is a word that means "no" or "not." Do not use two negatives to express one negative idea.

INCORRECT: We can't do nothing.

CORRECT: We can't do anything.

CORRECT: We can do nothing.

Negative Words

no	no one	never
none	nothing	neither
nobody	nowhere	

PRONOUN USAGE (See also Pronouns, pp. 332–335.)

I, me

When using *I* or *me* with nouns or other pronouns, always name yourself last.

Beth and I will leave.   Give the papers to Ron and me.

Read each question below. Then check your paper. Correct any mistakes you find. After you have corrected them, put a check mark in the box next to the question.

❑ **1.** Did I spell all words correctly?

❑ **2.** Did I indent each paragraph?

❑ **3.** Does each sentence state a complete thought?

❑ **4.** Are there any run-on sentences or fragments?

❑ **5.** Did I begin each sentence with a capital letter?

❑ **6.** Did I capitalize all proper nouns?

❑ **7.** Did I end each sentence with the correct end mark?

❑ **8.** Did I use commas, apostrophes, and quotation marks correctly?

Are there other problem areas you should watch for? Make your own proofreading checklist.

❑ _____

❑ _____

❑ _____

❑ _____

❑ _____

❑ _____

❑ _____

❑ _____

PROOFREADING MARKS

Mark	Explanation	Example
¶	Begin a new paragraph. Indent the paragraph.	¶The space shuttle landed safely after its five-day voyage. It glided to a smooth, perfect halt.
∧	Add letters, words, or sentences.	My ^best^ friend eats lunch with me ev^e^ry day.
∧)	Add a comma.	Carlton, my Siamese cat, has a mind of his own.
⟨⟨ ⟩⟩	Add quotation marks.	"Where do you want us to put the piano?" asked the gasping movers.
⊙	Add a period.	Don't forget to put a period at the end of every statement⊙
ℛ	Take out words, sentences, and punctuation marks. Correct spelling.	We ~~looked at and~~ admired the model air^a^planes.
/	Change a capital letter to a small letter.	We are studying about the Louisiana Purchase in /History class.
≡	Change a small letter to a capital letter.	The Nile ≡river in ≡africa is the longest river in the world.
∼	Reverse letters or words.	To comple∼et the task successfully, you must follow⟨carefully⟩ the steps.